D1082469

DATE DUE

41990

JAMES McNEILL
WHISTLER

Catalogue by FREDERICK A. SWEET

Paintings   Pastels   Watercolors
Drawings   Etchings
Lithographs

THE ART INSTITUTE OF CHICAGO

January 13, 1968 through February 25, 1968

MUNSON-WILLIAMS-PROCTOR INSTITUTE, Utica, N. Y.

March 17, 1968 through April 28, 1968

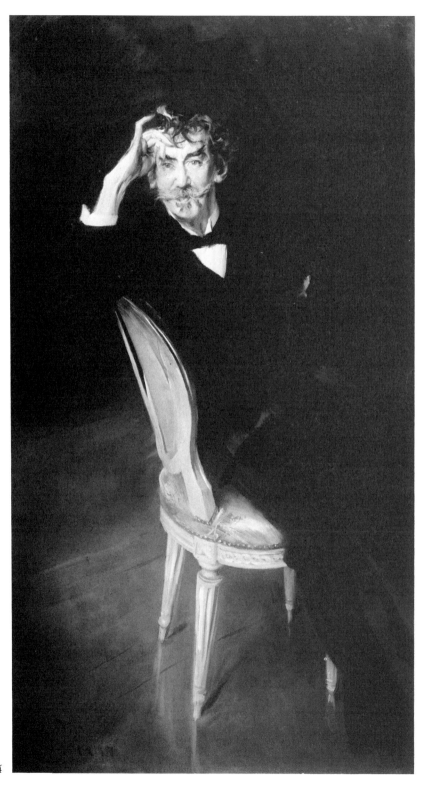

WHISTLER

COVER: NO. 5

The Little White Girl:
Symphony in White, No. 2.
Lent by the Trustees of the Tate Gallery, London.

FRONTISPIECE: NO. 214

Portrait of James McNeill Whistler
by Giovanni Boldini
Lent by The Brooklyn Museum

69

Design by RUGGLES/SWANSON/TACHI GRAPHIC SERVICES
Printed in the U.S.A. by H. L. RUGGLES & Co., Chicago

116

FOREWORD

In 1904, the year after his death, a major exhibition in the United States of the works of James McNeill Whistler was held at the Copley Society, Boston. Although other exhibitions of Whistler's art have been assembled, both in the United States and abroad, none of these, with the exception of that organized by the Arts Council of Great Britain in 1960, and displayed in New York at Knoedler Galleries, have shown the full range of Whistler's genius and the inventiveness of his creative spirit.

With the current focus on the role of the Impressionist and Post-Impressionist painters, Whistler's contribution and his originality has frequently been overlooked by art critics and art historians, and through this neglect, his influence on the art of future generations therefore has not been marked. Nevertheless, we should not overlook the fact that Whistler was among the first artists to establish a new credo of aesthetics in which art was not the reproduction of a visual image, but a creative act in itself. In fact, in "The Red Rag," written in 1878, Whistler said, "Art should be independent of all claptrap—should stand alone, and appeal to the artistic sense of eye or ear, without confounding this with emotions entirely foreign to it. . . ." Whistler attempted to do just this, and as such he is a direct precursor of modern aesthetics.

This exhibition has been assembled by Frederick A. Sweet, Curator of American Painting and Sculpture, The Art Institute of Chicago, and is the result of many years of research into the art of Whistler. The organization of an exhibition of Whistler's paintings must of necessity have limitations, due to prohibitions against lending in such institutions as the Freer Gallery of Art, the Frick Collection, the Isabella Stewart Gardner Museum, and the Grenville Winthrop Collection in the Fogg Art Museum, Harvard University, where some of Whistler's major paintings are to be found. Furthermore, restrictions of a different sort have also prevented the inclusion of such key works of Whistler as *The Artist's Mother* from the Louvre and the *Thomas Carlyle* from the City Art Gallery and Museum, Glasgow. Nevertheless the major museums of the United States, the Tate Gallery, London, the University of Glasgow, and many private collectors have made generous loans to make this exhibition a notable one. To all these lenders, The Art Institute of Chicago and the Munson-Williams-Proctor Institute, Utica, New York, extend their deepest appreciation.

The preparation of the catalogue has been the work of Frederick A. Sweet, who has been ably assisted by Mrs. Judith Di Meo and Miss Sandra Grung of the staff of The Art Institute of Chicago. We are very much indebted to Andrew McLaren Young of the University of Glasgow, the author of the forthcoming catalogue raisonné of Whistler's work, for many favors and for his invaluable assistance in advising us of the present whereabouts of some of Whistler's paintings.

This is the first major museum exhibition of the art of Whistler in over sixty years, and we hope that it will lead to a greater knowledge and appreciation of Whistler's achievements.

Charles C. Cunningham, Director, The Art Institute of Chicago
Edward H. Dwight, Director, Museum of Art, Munson-Williams-Proctor Institute, Utica, New York

LENDERS TO THE EXHIBITION

ADDISON GALLERY OF AMERICAN ART, ANDOVER, MASSACHUSETTS
ALBRIGHT-KNOX ART GALLERY, BUFFALO, NEW YORK
AMHERST COLLEGE, AMHERST, MASSACHUSETTS
ANONYMOUS
THE ART INSTITUTE OF CHICAGO
MR. GORDON T. BEAHAM, JR.
THE BROOKLYN MUSEUM
CALIFORNIA PALACE OF THE LEGION OF HONOR, SAN FRANCISCO
CINCINNATI ART MUSEUM
CITY ART MUSEUM OF ST. LOUIS
STERLING AND FRANCINE CLARK ART INSTITUTE, WILLIAMSTOWN,
    MASSACHUSETTS
CORCORAN GALLERY OF ART
CORNELL UNIVERSITY, ANDREW DICKSON WHITE MUSEUM OF ART
THE RIGHT HONOURABLE VISCOUNT COWDRAY
FOGG ART MUSEUM, HARVARD UNIVERSITY
RITA AND DANIEL FRAAD
HONOLULU ACADEMY OF ARTS
JOHN G. JOHNSON COLLECTION, PHILADELPHIA
LIBRARY OF CONGRESS, PRINTS AND PHOTOGRAPHS DIVISION
THE METROPOLITAN MUSEUM OF ART
MONCLAIR ART MUSEUM, NEW JERSEY
MUSEUM OF ART, CARNEGIE INSTITUTE, PITTSBURGH
MUSEUM OF ART, RHODE ISLAND SCHOOL OF DESIGN, PROVIDENCE
MUSEUM OF FINE ARTS, BOSTON
NATIONAL GALLERY OF ART, WASHINGTON, D.C.
THE NATIONAL GALLERY OF CANADA, OTTAWA
NEW BRITAIN MUSEUM OF AMERICAN ART, CONNECTICUT
PHILADELPHIA MUSEUM OF ART
MR. AND MRS. JOHN J. PIERREPONT
RANDOLPH-MACON WOMAN'S COLLEGE, LYNCHBURG, VIRGINIA
RIJKSMUSEUM, AMSTERDAM
SMITH COLLEGE MUSEUM OF ART, NORTHAMPTON, MASSACHUSETTS
MR. IRA SPANIERMAN
MRS. DIEGO SUAREZ
THE TATE GALLERY, LONDON
MRS. JOHN B. THAYER
MR. RONALD TREE
UNIVERSITY OF GLASGOW, SCOTLAND
THE UNIVERSITY OF MICHIGAN MUSEUM OF ART, ANN ARBOR
WADSWORTH ATHENEUM, HARTFORD, CONNECTICUT
THE CHILDREN OF MR. AND MRS. WILLIAM POTTER WEAR
WORCESTER ART MUSEUM, WORCESTER, MASSACHUSETTS

15 *The Artist in His Studio.*
   The Art Institute of Chicago

47

I should like to express my appreciation to Andrew McLaren Young, of the University of Glasgow, for his advice and valuable help in connection with this exhibition; and to Carl P. Barbier, of the University of Edinburgh, for his interesting comments on Whistler's relations with contemporary French artists. At the Art Institute, my special thanks go to Judith DiMeo for her exhaustive research in connection with the preparation of the catalogue entries, and to Sandra Grung for attending to the infinite details involved in assembling the exhibition. F.A.S

121

INTRODUCTION

Whistler the artist has been difficult to visualize, as he has always been seen in terms of Whistler the wit, Whistler the dandy, and Whistler the troublemaker. Furthermore, as an artist he has usually been regarded as an isolated phenomenon running counter to the trends of his day and having little relationship stylistically to any of his contemporaries. Behind Whistler's public image, which was often deplorable, emerges the artist who in the privacy of his studio was deadly serious, hard-working and severe in self-criticism. Careful study of Whistler's contemporaries both in France and in England reveals the fact that he was indeed subject to numerous influences and despite his own individuality was firmly embedded in the Victorian world. He was proud of being an American, of having attended West Point, and was deeply attached to his mother, whose simplicity of taste and whose abhorrence of ostentation had a marked effect on her son, at least in his attitude towards his art and his living, if not in his dress. His arrogance was perhaps learned as a boy from Russian nobles.

Joseph Pennell and his wife, Elizabeth Robbins Pennell, published in 1908 what still remains the standard life of Whistler, yet they are the very ones who are responsible for numerous misconceptions about the artist. Having come into his life late, they, as self-appointed Boswells, wanted to monopolize him and tended to disregard or minimize the influence of his friends and associates. In 1900 Whistler's publisher, William Heinemann, did to be sure ask them to write his biography. Although they recount all sorts of escapades, everything is kept well within the bounds of propriety. Jo and Maud are his models but there is never a hint that they were also his mistresses. Pennell, himself an etcher, had some understanding of Whistler the printmaker, but he had less understanding of Whistler the painter. Many others shared this view, with the result that Whistler was first appreciated for his etchings, and was not really honored as a painter until about 1890. His development as an artist has to be considered from three basic aspects: first of all that he was an American with a decided American viewpoint, which meant that he was always an outsider; secondly, that his training and first European contacts occurred in Paris; finally, that he spent the greater part of his mature life in London. Interwoven with the influences from these environments were elements which he had absorbed from classical, Dutch, Spanish and, above all, Japanese art.

Whistler was interested in drawing from the time he was a small boy of four; when he was ten his mother said it was hard to get him to put up his drawing and go to bed. As a result of his marked talent, he was entered in a course of drawing at the Academy of Fine Arts in St. Petersburg in April, 1845. His father, Major George Washington Whistler, had graduated from West Point in 1819 but resigned his commission in 1833. With the tremendous growth in railroads and the shortage of trained engineers, West Point graduates were allowed by the government to work for private corporations. In 1834 Major Whistler assumed the post of engineer to the Proprietors of Locks and Canals at Lowell, Massachusetts. The family moved into the Paul Moody house on Worthen Street where a son James was born July 10, 1834. On November 9 he was baptized in St. Anne's Episcopal Church with the name James Abbott. Two years later his brother William Gibbs McNeill Whistler was born in the same house. In 1837 they moved to Stonington, Connecticut, and in 1840 to Springfield, Massachusetts, in connection with Major Whistler's activities in the building of railroads. Then in 1842 he was invited by Czar Nicholas I of Russia to build a railroad from St. Petersburg to Moscow at a salary of $12,000 per year, princely for that day. They lived extremely well with several servants in addition to their own Irish maid, Mary. The boys James and William had a governess and a Swedish tutor. They enjoyed dancing school and in the winter skating on the Neva.

As the Winans Locomotive works of Baltimore furnished the equipment, members of the firm were in St. Petersburg and formed a nucleus of American families with whom the Whistlers were intimate. In so far as possible they tried to maintain an American way of life which, at least in the Whistler household, meant quiet Sundays with no reading other than the King James Version. Mrs. Whistler was a staunch Episcopalian but came from a prim, highland Scottish family, the McNeills of Barra, who had supported Prince Charles Edward. After "the Fortyfive" when the Stuarts were defeated at Culloden, the McNeills emigrated to North Carolina. Although the Whistler family were English from the upper Thames valley, they went to Ireland in the 16th century and had a considerable amount of Irish blood. Whistler liked to boast that he was

18

entirely Irish and Scottish and had no Anglo-Saxon blood. His grandfather John Whistler enlisted in the British army and was sent to the American colonies during the Revolution to join General Burgoyne, arriving just about in time to surrender at Saratoga, October 17, 1777. He was sent back to England, left the army and eloped with the daughter of Sir Edward Bishop. Having liked the Colonies, he returned with his wife, settled in Maryland and enlisted in the United States army and rose to the rank of Major. In 1803 while stationed at Detroit he was ordered to the mouth of the Chicago River to build Fort Dearborn. Earlier he had been stationed at Fort Wayne where in 1800 his son, George Washington Whistler, was born.

For the summer of 1847 Mrs. Whistler and the boys went to England and visited cousins whom they had also visited on their way to Russia. At that time Deborah, Major Whistler's daughter by his first marriage, had met Dr. Seymour Haden. They now became engaged and were married October 10, 1847. As James found the Russian winters hard and had suffered from rheumatic fever, the family spent another summer in England mostly on the Isle of Wight. In the fall James was left with the Hadens while the rest returned to St. Petersburg. Major Whistler, who had heart trouble, died on April 9, 1849. Mrs. Whistler and William went to England, picked up James, and they all returned to America settling on a farm in Pomfret, Connecticut, where the boys attended Christ Church Hall. With the family income reduced to $1,500 a year, the strictest economy had to be observed. At school James was constantly busy drawing. Upon graduating he decided that he wanted to go to West Point even though he was considered too small to be a military man. Through family connections he was able to obtain an appointment from President Fillmore on July 1, 1851. Although he was constantly getting into scrapes and disobeying the rules, he really enjoyed the life at the Military Academy, had numerous friends and had a profound respect for the efficiency of military procedures. Interest in drawing continued and he stood first in the course given by Robert W. Weir but he was incapable of learning to sit a horse and even worse was his deficiency in chemistry. What was more serious was the fact that he had accumulated 218 demerits which was eighteen more than the law allowed; as a result he was dismissed June 16, 1854.

Through his older half-brother George Whistler, who had married Julia Winans, he was able to obtain an apprenticeship with the Winans Locomotive works in Baltimore. George and his brother-in-law and partner Thomas Winans took turns having James live with them and tried to interest him in directing his talent towards drawing designs for locomotives. Young Whistler preferred to use the drafting boards for drawings of his own fancy and had no interest in the life of an apprentice. He was soon off to Washington where he was given a job with the United States Coast and Geodetic Survey which was headed by Captain Benham, an old friend of his father's. Here he worked for $1.50 per day from November 17, 1854, to February 12, 1855. He was always late and often absent, was much entertained in Washington circles and thoroughly enjoyed himself, but was the despair of his employer. At this time, however, he had the finest of training in etching and learned the basic principles of printmaking which he found invaluable in later years. Two plates can be attributed to him: *Coast Survey, No. 1* and *Coast Survey, No. 2, Anacapa Island*. He also did a very Rembrandtesque lithograph called *The Standard Bearer*.

While in Washington Whistler had a studio, painted a few portraits, but longed to be an art student in Paris. He finally convinced his mother that he must go abroad to study and, with the promise of a $350 a year allowance, set out for Paris where he arrived in the fall of 1855 after visiting the Hadens in London en route. In Paris he could escape from the decidedly puritanical influence of his mother as well as the watchful eye of his sister. He wanted to be a bohemian and read avidly Henri Murger's *Scènes de la Vie de Bohème*. There were few American students in Paris at that time although there were several from England. Whistler had one great advantage in that he was fluent in French, learned when he was a boy in St. Petersburg, which enabled him to mingle at once with the French students and enter into their life. He much preferred them in any case to the English whom he found stuffy and more interested in cooking English-type food and doing gymnastics than in entering into the café and studio life of Paris. He spent about two years in the *atelier* of Charles Gabriel Gleyre, who was a follower of Raphael and Ingres, but was dilatory in attendance, although he learned a basic principle which he followed all his life, namely to arrange all the colors that

75

would be needed on a palette before beginning a picture. In that way full attention could be given to the painting without stopping to mix colors.

The English students, Thomas Armstrong, Thomas R. Lamont, Edward John Poynter and George du Maurier were known as the "Paris Gang." Whistler, too, was considered a part of it but did not associate with them very much, preferring his French friends, among whom were musicians and poets as well as artists. He also kept up with contemporary French literature, especially poetry. For a time he had a relationship with a tempestuous modiste named Héloïse, who was model and mistress.

He learned little in the *atelier*, for Gleyre came only once a week to give a perfunctory look at his students' work. By keeping his eyes and ears open and by meeting a variety of stimulating people he knew he would learn more. Whistler was already attracting attention with his bizarre dress—wide-brimmed, low-crown straw hat with dangling ribbon and white duck suit. He met Charles Baudelaire and was influenced by his poetry and learned that art could be original and creative. Lecoq de Boisbaudran was another exciting acquaintance who taught him that drawing from memory stimulates the imagination. While copying in the Louvre one day in 1858 Whistler met Fantin-Latour who became one of his closest friends and had a profound influence on him. Fantin introduced him to Alphonse Legros, whom he later urged to settle in England. Of greater significance was Fantin's introduction to Gustave Courbet who said of him, "Il a du talent, le petit Whistler." He also owed to Fantin meeting the English poet Algernon Charles Swinburne, a frequent visitor to Paris and an admirer of Baudelaire. In 1857 Whistler went to Manchester to see the Old Master Exhibition which included fourteen paintings by or attributed to Velázquez whose low-keyed palette had great appeal for him. He was also working hard with etching and at first made some attempt to follow Rembrandt, and the contemporary French artist Charles Jacque had some influence on him. In 1858 he brought out *Twelve Etchings from Nature* usually referred to as "the French Set." These brought him his first recognition, which was indeed thoroughly justified for he was truly competent in this medium due to his early training in Washington. As a painter he still had much to learn. In 1859 he painted *At the Piano*, which in its low-keyed harmony and quiet mood was much influenced by his new friend Fantin-Latour and, no doubt reflects his interest in 17th-century Dutch interiors by Pieter de Hooch and Vermeer. Although the picture was rejected by the Salon of that year, it was shown with the work of other rejected artists at François Bonvin's studio where Courbet saw it and commented favorably. The picture was accepted by the Royal Academy in 1860. Although frequently returning to France, Whistler settled in London where he made long visits at the Hadens but also spent much time at an inn in Wapping, in which area his early Thames etchings and paintings were done. He depicted the most ordinary scenes of waterfront or river life but he never treated the people as "quaint" or as "characters," they are shown at ease and at home in their environment. Whistler went very much against the trend of mid-Victorian England as neither his painting nor his prints ever told a story or pointed a moral. It was inconceivable that a picture could be admired purely for its own sake. "Art for art's sake" was a concept yet to be born but Whistler was already anticipating this point of view. Théophile Gautier had already formulated the theory in regard to literature; the painters were soon to follow. Charles Baudelaire had a similar idea when he said, "Poetry has no other end but itself." As Whistler knew him in Paris, he had surely read *Les Fleurs du Mal*, which was published in 1857.

An important early painting was *Wapping* of 1861 showing the boats in the Thames and in the foreground three figures, one of whom is Joanna Hiffernan (This is the correct spelling as indicated by letters and documents signed by her. The form usually seen, "Heffernan," is incorrect, according to Professor Barbier.) who was his model and mistress. This has the realism of Courbet but with a very elaborate structure of verticals and diagonals which form a web-like background for the figures. Going back to Paris with Jo he painted her as *The White Girl*. Although rejected at The Royal Academy in 1862 and at the Salon of 1863, it was shown at the Salon des Refusés where it was admired by artists but laughed at by the public. She stood on a bearskin rug against a white hanging and was dressed in a flowing white gown totally unlike the crinolines of the day. Her red hair hung over her shoulders. Who was this strange, ethereal creature who was neither a contemporary nor historical personage; neither a classical goddess nor a Roman matron? She might perhaps belong to the medieval world; and, in fact, her languid

107

100

8

remoteness and her introspective gaze place her close to the Pre-Raphaelites. Whistler was of course familiar with their paintings in England and first met Dante Gabriel Rossetti in 1862 but he was no medievalist and had little sympathy with the group. That he was influenced by them is apparent. *The White Girl* may also be considered a sort of devotional tribute for, as Mallarmé indicated, an abundance of hair was a symbol of love.

Early in 1863 he leased 7 Lindsey Row (now 101 Cheyne Walk), Chelsea, where he set up housekeeping with Jo. His mother arrived from America late in the year and spent the rest of her life in England. Jo came to the house as model but now had quarters elsewhere. Mrs. Whistler was probably too innocent to be aware of the relationship; in any case she was too tactful ever to mention it.

Madame de Soye, who had lived in the Orient, opened a shop called *"La Porte Chinoise"* in 1862 at 220 rue de Rivoli in Paris. Here Whistler, as well as Fantin-Latour, the de Goncourts, Manet and others bought Japanese prints, fans, Chinese costumes and blue-and-white porcelain. Whistler was an avid collector of all of these items and was the first to make them appreciated in London. (No doubt he recalled the collections of Oriental porcelain which he had seen as a boy in the Imperial palaces of Russia). He did a series of paintings of languid women wearing Chinese costumes, surrounded by Oriental screens and porcelains, looking dreamily at a print or at a vase which one pretends to paint or, as in the case of *La Princesse du Pays de la Porcelaine*, limply holding a Japanese fan. These are examples of Whistler's fusion of disparate concepts which occur frequently in his work, for surely these are Pre-Raphaelite ladies who have forsaken the medieval world for the Oriental. This is, however, merely the Orientalism of studio trappings; and, despite the exotic overtones, is essentially Victorian. Whistler has not yet learned the Oriental view of space although in *La Princesse* he does recall figures by Utamaro. At this period he painted *The Little White Girl*, again with Jo as model, but this time leaning against a mantel, her red hair falling over a white dress of curious make. She is the aloof, unattainable, Pre-Raphaelite maiden who holds a Japanese fan and gazes listlessly at a blue-and-white jar and red lacquer teapot.

Official art in England, the art approved by the Royal Academy, was in the hands of Frederic Leighton, Edward John Poynter and Lawrence Alma-Tadema whose highly finished canvases were concerned largely with scenes from classical antiquity. The Elgin marbles in the British Museum were an ever-handy source of inspiration. Another painter of classical subjects, Albert Joseph Moore, had revolutionary ideas — his pictures did not tell a story. He was concerned primarily with the beauty of classical subjects and in arranging his single or small groups of figures to make a perfectly balanced design. Whistler was very much impressed by Moore's *The Marble Seat,* which was shown in the Royal Academy of 1865, with the result that he and Moore became great friends and Whistler's numerous classical subjects show Moore's influence. He once said that he considered Albert Moore the finest of the English painters.

Whistler made a trip to Valparaiso in 1866 the reasons for which remain unexplained. Chile at the time was struggling for independence from Spain. Could it be that Whistler, as a romantic American, felt the need to go to the aid of the oppressed just as Samuel Gridley Howe, American surgeon and humanitarian, had gone to Greece in the 1820's? Late in the year he moved to 2 Lindsey Row (now 96 Cheyne Walk) where he had a blue dining room with dark blue dado and doors. It was here that he began to paint "Nocturnes," the first being called *Twilight on the Ocean,* shown in the International Exposition in Paris in 1867. At this time he had a fight with his brother-in-law, Seymour Haden, who was also in Paris, and knocked him through a plate glass window. They never spoke again.

He sent to the Royal Academy *Symphony in White, No. III,* which was his first use of symphony, or any musical term. The composition of two figures so carefully placed and perfectly balanced shows the influence of Albert Moore. On the other hand, the intrusion of flowers at the right-hand side is a Japanese mannerism. In the late 60's and early 70's he did a whole series of small oils and pastels of classical figures deriving both from Moore and from the study of Tanagra statuettes; but there is again the fusion of the Oriental, for many of these women carry Japanese fans or parasols.

In 1871 he published the sixteen etchings of the "Thames Set," and continued a series of atmospheric paintings of the Thames which he first called "Moonlights" then, probably at Leyland's suggestion, "Nocturnes." In these etchings Whistler caught the atmosphere of the river front, the boats and bridges and the people associated with river life. His etching style at this period is clean-cut rather than atmospheric and his line is firm and sure. Samuel P. Avery, who was the Art Commissioner for the United States at the Paris Exposition of 1867, met Whistler through George Lucas of Baltimore, and was the first American to collect Whistler's etchings and greatly encourage him to continue in this medium with which he had such facility. Whistler was extremely fussy about the printing of his plates, which his avid pupil, Mortimer Menpes, has described in detail. In the early period he liked a full black proof; then came the drypoint period when he liked a cool, silvery effect suggestive of pastel; then, in the Venice period, he liked a warmer tone. He had no use for *retroussage*, dragging a cloth across the plate to pull some ink from the grooves to give an artificially induced richer effect.

Nearby in Chelsea lived Walter Greaves and his brother Harry, boatbuilders, Whistler hired to row him on the Thames. They also studied painting with him and Walter, at least, achieved a fair degree of competency. They usually started out at twilight and were often on the river most of the night. Whistler was fascinated by the foggy or misty effects of the river in fading light and the nights with twinkling lights from a dock building or a boat riding at anchor. At such times space became compressed and distances were deceptive. In putting his impressions on canvas from memory he made use of the Japanese concept of space as a well-balanced design in which perspective plays no part. Whistler admired the paintings of Claude, who had treated sunsets in an atmospheric manner, and he had great regard for Canaletto. Although critical of Turner, he was very familiar with his work and must inevitably have been influenced by him. One is tempted to find a close affinity with Chinese painting. Although the great Eumorfopoulos collection had not yet been formed, there were Chinese paintings available at this time in the Victoria and Albert Museum. While their quality was not the highest their concept of atmosphere and mystery done in a seemingly casual manner, merely suggesting a scene, would have appealed to Whistler. One of Whistler's friends in Paris was the composer Claude Debussy, and they had a mutual admiration for each other. Mood, tone and "color," they agreed, could be as well expressed in music as with the brush.

Stéphane Mallarmé, the French Symbolist poet, in 1888 became perhaps Whistler's most intimate friend and one of the few people with whom he never quarrelled. They carried on a lengthy and intimate correspondence, always in French, and, when Whistler was in Paris, he was the most honored guest at Mallarmé's famous "*Mardis*," Tuesday evening gatherings at his apartment on the rue de Rome where numerous writers and a few artists met to listen to the master expound in a quiet but compelling way on Symbolism. Whistler had wanted to meet the poet as he admired his poems, a few of which had been published, before *L'Après Midi d'un Faune* in 1876. *L'Azur* appeared in *Le Parnasse Contemporain* in 1866 and treated of the mysteries of night. Mallarmé had once said, "Do not paint the object but the effect which it produces." His work was criticized for obscurity and for being in defiance of all the rules of reason and art. He said the power of poetry is not in precise images but in its suggestiveness. These Symbolist concepts can surely be applied to Whistler's Nocturnes, in which he took as a point of departure the hazy effects of the Thames at night, and developed his theme with subtle tones into a completely creative composition which suggested the mysteries of the night but existed as a symbolic representation to be admired entirely for its own sake regardless of any specific references to observed reality.

It is interesting to note that Mallarmé and Whistler shared a devotion to the work of Edgar Allan Poe (who incidentally had also been discharged from West Point).

Arrangement in Grey and Black No. 1: the Artist's Mother, probably begun in 1867, was finished in 1872 and was accepted under protest at the Royal Academy. After this Whistler never submitted again and he was never elected to the Academy.

He composed the painting with disarming simplicity with Japanese compartmented spacial relationships in mind, and the profile silhouette most deftly placed. There is an echo here of early Victorian painting, such as *The Travelling Companions* by Augustus Leopold Egg. Shortly after this, he painted Thomas Carlyle in a similar, although more concentrated pose, with greater angularity to the silhouette, which gives the picture more character.

R850.

21

About this time, Maud Franklin replaced Jo as model and mistress. Whistler's mode of life was by no means simply the result of having adopted the French attitude towards such matters at an early age. Victorian England's strict sense of propriety had been artificially imposed by the newly prosperous industrial middle class; underneath a thin surface of respectability can be found unlimited license, as attested by the revelations of the unidentified author of *My Secret Life*.

At the time he was doing the Carlyle portrait he was also working on *Miss Cicely Alexander*. She is posed standing in a crisply-starched white and gray muslin dress holding a gray hat. Here the subtle, muted tones and the transparent glazes indicate Whistler's great admiration for Velázquez. The figure is carefully integrated with the background in which the parallel bands of floor, dado and wall seem all to be on one plane. Space is pictorial and not atmospheric. This was the most controversial picture of the group which comprised his first one-man exhibition at the Flemish Gallery, 48, Pall Mall, which opened June 6, 1874. To the public the picture was a strange, ghostly, colorless, unfinished canvas.

One of his most brilliant Nocturnes was one of fireworks at night at Cremorne Gardens, a famous London pleasure haunt. Sparks and flares of light momentarily illuminate the night sky and evoke the mystery of dimly revealed forms. Such a painting anticipates the Expressionists of the early 20th century. What he was interested in as he said was line, form and color. Cremorne Gardens had merely furnished the motif from which he developed a creative painting which was to be admired for its own sake without regard to any specific associations. During the summer of 1877 Whistler exhibited this and several other paintings at the Grosvenor Gallery, recently opened by Sir Coutts Lindsay. John Ruskin, considered the arbiter of taste in England, now well past his prime, had never bothered to look at Whistler's work but went to the exhibition. Utterly enraged by *The Falling Rocket* he wrote a most insulting review in *Fors Clavigera*, in which he accused Whistler of "cockney impudence" and that in *Falling Rocket* he was "flinging a pot of paint in the public's face." Whistler sued him for libel in what proved to be the most sensational art trial of the century. As might be expected, there was not much sympathy for Whistler's work, yet libel was clearly indicated. Whistler won a Pyrrhic victory with a farthing damages without costs. Ruskin's friends paid his court costs, but no one helped Whistler, who was financially ruined and had to sell the White House which the architect, E. W. Godwin, had built for him in 1878. What was at stake in the Whistler-Ruskin trial was the whole question of "Art for Art's Sake." This might do in frivolous France, but there was no place for such ideas in stolid, prosperous Victorian England. Had not the good Prince Consort set a strong moral tone on the arts? Even the Pre-Raphaelites could be admired for their high finish and some sort of a story, although it was often rather exotic and there were overtones of smouldering emotions. Whistler, who was concerned neither with narrative nor with moralizing, evoked an atmosphere and a mood with great subtlety of tone and carefully arranged harmonies which could indeed be admired for their own sake, but few could appreciate this.

By the later 70's the writings of Algernon Swinburne and Walter Pater on Art for Art's Sake began to make an impression but the results were ludicrous. Thus the Aesthetic Movement was born, in which people cluttered their houses with William Morris desks, textiles and wall paper, frail bamboo chairs, blue-and-white porcelain, Japanese fans and prints. Women wore medieval or classical costumes and went around sad-eyed and melancholy. The whole thing was a travesty on what Whistler had tried to establish as good taste. In his own houses there were plain yellow, gray or Antwerp blue walls, a few prints carefully placed, one blue-and-white bowl on the dining-room table, no awkward or heavy over-stuffed furniture, "If you want to be comfortable," he said, "go to bed."

Whistler constantly returned to Paris and kept in with the group there. He was aware that the Impressionists painted what they liked and did not cater to a public. He knew and admired Degas, who was the only person who could take him down, and said of Whistler when he was acting up, "You behave as if you had no talent." Whistler had no sympathy with the Impressionists' methods but he admired their independence. He was a friend of Monet, but his associations were more with the writers, Stéphane Mallarmé and others whom he met at the *Mardis*. Comte Robert de Montesquiou was also a close friend and he painted his portrait. Marcel Proust admired his work and made him one of the component parts of his fictional painter Elstir, a name which he took from Neils Elstiern, a painter, parody of Whistler, in Camille Mauclair's *Le Soleil des Morts*. While Whistler's associations in France kept him in touch with new movements, he felt very much an outsider and was frustrated by the fact that he could not fine a place in either England or France.

Through Rossetti, Whistler had met the "Liverpool Medici" Frederick Leyland, a wealthy shipowner. He painted portraits of Mr. and Mrs. Leyland and decorated the dining room of their London house in Prince's Gate. Leyland had bought *La Princesse du Pays de la Porcelaine* and Whistler felt that the dining room should be decorated to harmonize with the picture. While Leyland was away, he completely painted over the old Spanish leather in a brilliant scheme of gold and blue peacocks. Leyland was horrified at the result and there was a squabble over the amount to be paid, which resulted in bitter enmity between them. Known as the "Peacock Room," it is now in the Freer Gallery in Washington. Whistler's decorative scheme, based on the sweeping curves of peacock feathers, anticipated Art Nouveau. He then painted a cruel caricature of Leyland as a peacock playing the piano, which he called *The Gold Scab or Eruption in Frilthy Lucre*.

A fortunate circumstance arose when the Fine Arts Society commissioned Whistler to do twelve etchings of Venice to be delivered in three months. Whistler spent fourteen months in Venice, and did not only many etchings, but also pastels and watercolors. Maud went with him and prepared his meals. The work he did there more than anything else helped him to achieve a position in the art world. A group of twelve etchings was shown at the Fine Arts Society in December, 1880, and, although the critics were still hostile, people began to buy. Whistler's Venetian etchings show a complete change in style. The subject matter —doorways with elaborate architectural detail, the lagoon, side canals and out-of-the-way parts of Venice—provided him with a challenge. He treated these themes with the utmost delicacy, using a spidery line, lively curves, and often wiped the plates to give a tone. He was fond, too, of using fine old paper which gave richness and a subtle variety of off-whites. When printed with brown inks, which he favored, the result seemed almost antique and was completely suited to the subject matter. Some of the little figures in gondolas are reminiscent of Jacques

Callot, the early 17th century French painter and engraver. Canaletto, it must be remembered, was also greatly admired by Whistler.

On returning to London he took a house at 13 Tite Street where he painted the walls yellow and again bought blue-and-white china and old silver. His innovation of Sunday noon breakfasts, begun at Lindsey Row, was now revived, as he had become a personality people wanted to know. Four years later he moved into a studio at 454A Fulham Road, but lived with Maud in The Vale, Chelsea.

Now that he had re-established himself, Whistler hoped to be in great demand to do portraits of prominent people, but in this he was disappointed. He was unreasonably exacting to his sitters and often quarrelsome. While he painted two distinguished portraits of Lady Meux, a third was never finished, due to an argument. One, which Whistler called his "beautiful Black Lady," was a dramatic composition in black and white with a black evening gown and an ermine-lined cape. His portrait of Lady Archibald Campbell, distinguished and unusual in its pose, was one of his most dashing achievements, yet the sitter was not pleased. In his portrait of the famous violinist Pablo de Sarasate he conveys the dramatic expectancy of a stage performance about to begin and makes effective use of the contrasting black and white of formal dress.

On January 31, 1881, his mother died at Hastings where she lived during her later years because of ill health.

On the evening of February 20, 1885, Whistler in faultless evening dress delivered at Prince's Hall, London, the "Ten O'Clock," his famous lecture summing up in beautifully polished prose his theories of aesthetics. He held his audience and made a profound impression, pointing out that people do not look *at* a picture, but *through* it, seeking for something to improve their mental or moral state. Art, he said, had existed in all periods and had only been vanquished in modern times when the manufacturers of Birmingham and Manchester substituted the cheap, machine-made imitation. Nature contains the elements of art and the artist must choose just as the composer selects his notes. The poetry that evening mists produce when "the tall chimneys become campanili and the warehouses are palaces in the night," can be appreciated only by the artist. Literary men fail to see the painter's poetry in which form and color have been put into perfect harmony. There are too many "experts" who are triumphant at ascertaining the date of an object but are utterly oblivious to its artistic significance. Art can not be understood by everyone; only vulgarity is common to all. "The Dilettante stalks abroad. The amateur is loosed. The voice of the aesthete is heard in the land, and catastrophe is upon us." Art is not concerned with the scenic beauty of Switzerland but rather with a piece of Chinese blue porcelain or a painting by Velázquez. Art does not concern the multitude but only the few.

The lecture was well received and was repeated several times. Stéphane Mallarmé translated it into French and read it aloud in Berthe Morisot's salon.

During the following year the *Set of Twenty-six Etchings* was exhibited at Dowdeswell's and included twenty-one Venetian scenes and five English subjects. Again the critics were hostile but numerous sales were made. His exhibitions were always beautifully hung in a specially designed setting. In this instance he used white walls, yellow hangings and yellow flowers. Yellow and white livery was provided for the doorman and Whistler wore yellow socks.

His friend the architect E. W. Godwin died, and in 1888 Whistler married his widow Beatrix, called Trixie, and began what was to prove a completely happy married life. Soon after this they moved to 21 Cheyne Walk. Maud Franklin was still on the scene but had to step aside in favor of Trixie who was a strong character and ruled the day. Whistler's acquisition of a wife coincided with his rise in popularity and his being held in high regard in both France and England.

In 1891 the Corporation of Glasgow purchased the *Carlyle* for a thousand guineas; his first sale to a public institution and an event which added greatly to Whistler's prestige. A few months later the Luxembourg bought the *Mother* for four thousand francs, a modest amount, but again adding greatly to his standing. Mallarmé had been instrumental in bringing about the purchase. At this time Whistler was raised from a Chevalier (awarded in 1889) to an Officier of the Légion d'Honneur.

In the spring of 1892 he had a one-man exhibition at Goupil's in London, and the critics were unanimous in their praise, as they were in the exhibition held in the Champ-de-Mars, in Paris.

The Whistlers decided to transfer their residence to Paris and in 1893 moved to the Hôtel du Bon Lafontaine while waiting for an apartment at 110, rue du Bac to be done over for them. Here Whistler was commissioned by Sir William Eden to do his wife's portrait. Again there was a dispute over the payment and a long drawn out controversy ending in a law suit. Whistler won and was allowed to retain the painting, thus establishing a precedent.

One of Whistler's finest achievements was in the field of lithography, which he began in 1878 under Thomas Way, a lithographic printer. After an interval he took it up again in 1887 and over a period of ten years did about a hundred and fifty, many of them with a small number of proofs. This phase of his work so little known deserves the highest consideration. Drawing in the most spirited way, he used a stump as well as a pencil and obtained effects that no one before him had ever succeeded in achieving. Although some are of the Thames or of a tea table in his Chelsea garden, many are scenes in Paris: cafés, the Louvre and especially the Luxembourg Gardens. Some are single figures of women in the most elegant dress or groups of figures all very much *hommes du monde*. There are also incisive portraits of men such as his pupil, Walter Sickert, and the sensitive portrayal of his friend Mallarmé. There is a decided French spirit here which reminds us how close his contacts with the French had always been. During the nineties, when he lived in **Paris,** these associations were reconfirmed. Some of the single figures have the dash of Paul Helleu, who had done such a beautiful drypoint portrait of Whistler. Others show a close affinity to Pierre Bonnard. Through his lithographs Whistler, towards the end of his career, attains a position of the highest distinction.

Whistler was also a distinguished book designer and went to great pains with page layouts with very wide margins and the block of type placed with a perfection of asymmetrical balance. His butterfly emblem, first seen on an invitation in 1874, was used as a decorative motif, and as such may be considered to be Art Nouveau. Whistler knew Arthur H. Muckmurdo, active in the Arts and Crafts Movement, who did designs for *The Hobby Horse*, but he thought them too elaborate. More to his taste would have been the simplified designs advocated by

79

45

Maurice Denis, one of the *Nabis*, who did the layout in 1890 for Paul Verlaine's *Sagesse*, the earliest of Art Nouveau books. He did not believe in having publications hand-done with an over-elaboration of decoration, as favored by the Kelmscott Press whose first publication appeared in 1891; on the contrary, he used commercial type and the simplest of brown paper binding with a yellow cloth spine. In 1890 he assembled several previous pamphlets and published *The Gentle Art of Making Enemies*, and in 1899 issued in Paris *Eden versus Whistler: The Baronet and the Butterfly*. These were revelations in the studied simplicity of good book design.

Much of his time in the last years was devoted to etchings and to lithographs, subject matter for which he could always find in abundance in the streets of London and Paris, on trips to Holland, Belgium or to French and English seaside resorts. Numerous tiny oils were done, especially in the eighties, in which he managed in the smallest space to paint a powerful seascape, idyllic beach scenes, or intimate views of city shops and doorways. He was now prosperous and, with freedom from financial worries, tended to put aside anything which did not interest him. In Dorset in 1895 he painted *Little Rose of Lyme Regis* and the *Master Smith*, both of which he handled with brilliance and, perhaps because of their smaller scale, carried through without the difficulties which he encountered in his last full-length portraits, such as that of George Vanderbilt.

Trixie became seriously ill with cancer (a fact that Whistler would never admit) and a few months after their return to England died at Hampstead on May 10, 1896. After this he was very restless. He travelled to Holland, back and forth to France and to Corsica, for his health.

One constructive effort that he carried on after Trixie's death was to open the Académie Carmen at 6, Passage Stanislas, Paris. This gave him an opportunity to expound his ideas that one starts a painting with palette all arranged and the finished concept already in mind. He installed Trixie's sister and mother in the Paris apartment and continued to maintain studios and living quarters in both Paris and London. His last years were increasingly beset with illness. In April, 1903, the University of Glasgow conferred on him an honorary doctor's degree but he was unable to attend. He died shortly after, on July 17 and was buried in Chiswick Cemetery.

THE "SOCIETE DES TROIS"

The 7th October 1858 was to prove an important day in the lives of three artists who were to be closely associated till the middle 1860's: Whistler, Fantin-Latour and Legros. On that day, in the Louvre, the genial and bohemian Whistler of the large-brimmed hat came over to speak to the gentle unassuming Fantin who was engaged on copying Veronese's *Marriage Feast at Cana*. That same evening Fantin introduced his new friend to some of the habitués of the Café Molière, which included Legros, Scholderer, Carolus-Duran and Astruc, and to them Whistler showed the "French Set" etchings just completed after a tour of France, Luxembourg and the Rhineland in the company of Ernest Delaunoy. Within a few days, as further meetings took place at the Café Molière or at Andler Keller's where Courbet reigned, it became clear that Whistler was "one of them", one of that determined band of young "realists", who looked to Courbet for a lead in their fight against academic standards prevailing alike in studio and Salon, and who, though respectful of Delacroix, rejected the trappings of Romanticism in an effort to reflect in their art an honest concern for and reaction to everyday life. In keeping with their admiration for Spanish painting (especially Velázquez) and the pioneering efforts of such as Bonvin and Ribot, their paintings were generally set in a low key and subjects treated reflected sobriety and tranquillity. These last characteristics certainly featured in the pictures which Legros, Fantin and Whistler prepared for the 1859 Salon; yet consider the choice of subject or treatment of the *Angelus*, of Fantin's double portrait of his sisters Marie and Nathalie, of Whistler's *At the Piano*, and one already discerns in each a distinctive preoccupation which passing years only accentuated: with Legros it was naïveté conveying deep and simple religious faith, with Fantin honest portraiture of his subject coupled with suffused treatment of atmosphere, and with Whistler compositional arrangement, harmony and painterly qualities.

Very soon the three artists were drawn into a close association, later christened by Whistler the "Société des Trois." According to a recent critic, it "existed mainly as a sort of mutual protection and admiration society." This is to misunderstand the strength and practical nature of the association, to underestimate the impact which this ginger group had in forging links between the Paris avant-garde and English literary and artistic circles, and also to deny the part which this close bond had in determining the future of all three men.

The beginnings of the association are not well documented, partly because historians of the modern movement have concentrated on the Café de Bade and the Café Guerbois to the neglect of the earlier activity which centered in 1858 and 1859 on Andler's and the Café Molière. Still we know that on meeting Fantin and Legros Whistler introduced such English friends as Armstrong and Poynter to the Café Molière, and that he in turn quickly met a wide circle of French artists and critics. Besides earlier acquaintances such as H. Martin, Oulevey and Drouet, by 1859 Whistler had come to know Courbet, Bracquemond, Bonvin, Ribot, Regamey, Myionnet, Duranty, Chamfleury, Ottin, Sinet, Echerny and Valton.

Here are some of the practical steps which Whistler took to relieve the indigence of his two friends. The record is impressive, though considerable credit must go to his brother-in-law, Seymour Haden, a ready host and patron to a number of French artists.

In July 1859 a dejected Fantin, who had only succeeded in raising two francs for a still life at the Hôtel des Ventes, is persuaded to come to London. There he undergoes a whole range of new experiences as Whistler and Haden show him the life of the capital, introduce him to museums, exhibitions and concerts. Taken to the Café Suisse, he meets French expatriates including Félix Pyat. Haden initiates him to etching, buys two of his studies and commissions a Louvre copy. The visit succeeded for a while in raising Fantin's spirit as may be gathered from a letter to his parents which he signed: "henri Fantin la Tour qui sait maintenant ce qu'il vaut!!!...." The elation was short-lived. Back in Paris, Fantin reverted to his more usual frame of mind; as he told Whistler, existence seemed pointless, though he still cared to live "à cause de cette diable de peinture."

In the autumn of 1860, while working in London on *Wapping*, the painting where Joanna Hiffernan appears for the first time, Whistler put Ridley in contact with Fantin. The two became friends; Fantin painted Ridley's portrait, one of three pictures accepted for the 1861 Salon; and it was through Ridley that Fantin met Edwin Edwards, another of Whistler's friends.

Late in 1860 it was Legros's turn to be invited to London. He stayed with the Hadens. Whistler introduced him to a number of artists and patrons, among them Edwards for whom he painted and etched the drawing room at Sunbury. Having sold a number of works Legros returned to Paris and seriously considered the possibility of making a living in England.

At the beginning of July 1861 Fantin came over for a longer stay. As Whistler was ill with rheumatic fever, he stayed first with Haden at Hook's country home in Witley, Surrey, then with the Edwards at Sunbury. He sold the pictures he had brought, Haden giving a 1,000 francs for a large copy of the *Marriage Feast at Cana*. At Sunbury where he felt particularly at home he painted a number of flower pieces and started Mrs. Edwards's portrait. Towards the end of August he returned to Paris with Whistler.

By 1863 Whistler had widened his circle of friends to include the Pre-Raphaelites and most of the wealthy Greeks in London: the Coronios, Cassavettis, Cavafys, Lascardis and Spartalis. From Alexander Ionides and Dilberoglou he obtained orders for Fantin; in March he took *The White Girl* to Paris and introduced Swinburne to Manet and Fantin. Next he took the impecunious Legros first for six weeks to Amsterdam where they admired Rembrandt, then on to his London home at 7 Lindsey Row where Legros stayed till the end of the year. Legros came to know Rossetti, then Swinburne, renewed acquaintance with Alexander Ionides and his two sons who bought works from him and commissioned portraits. By the summer Legros had so many orders from the other members of the Greek Colony that Whistler urged Fantin to come over and share in the bonanza—in three or four weeks Legros had made 8,000 francs. Legros's future was assured. He resolved to settle in England and married Frances R. Hodgson the following year.

What of Fantin? Having urged him on several occasions to raise the price of his work, Whistler went to Paris and brought Fantin over to London in early July 1864. Within a week Ionides had paid 2,000 francs for the *Scene from Tannhäuser*, exhibited at the Salon, and 500 for two flower pieces. Soon Fantin, like Legros, had as much work as he could cope with. For a month the 'Société des Trois' worked all day at 7 Lindsey Row and were invited out most evenings. Fantin's comment was: "Nous faisons une vie impossible tous les trois dans l'atelier de Whistler. On se croirait à Nangasaki, ou dans le palais d'Eté, la Chine, le Japon, c'est splendide." After a fortnight at Sunbury in the company of Legros, Fantin was taken by Whistler to Mitton Hall in Lancashire where he succeeded in making a flattering portrait of a not so young Mrs. Potter for which he received 1,300 francs. They were back at Lindsey Row on the 11 September. Fantin spent a few more days with Whistler before going on to Sunbury to paint flower-pieces and complete Mrs. Edwards's portrait—he stayed till the middle of October in the congenial company of the Edwards, and grew closer to those who in the coming years were to play an increasing part in his fortunes.

Space forces me to close this all too brief glimpse of the "Société des Trois" which lasted until 1867, by which time Whistler and Fantin had each broken with Legros. Whistler and Fantin gradually drifted apart after the former's return from Valparaiso so that by 1869 Fantin had to confess that he was no longer able to understand Whistler's artistic life.

Carl Paul Barbier
Reader in French
University of Edinburgh

11

CHRONOLOGY

1834   July 10. Born Lowell, Massachusetts.

1837   Stonington, Connecticut.

1840   Springfield, Massachusetts.

1843   St. Petersburg, Russia, where his father, Major George Washington Whistler, was the engineer for building a railroad to Moscow at the request of Czar Nicholas I.

1845   Enrolled in art classes at Imperial Academy, St. Petersburg.

1847   Summer in England.
October 10 his half-sister Deborah married Dr. Seymour Haden.

1848   Summer in England.

1849   April 9 Major Whistler died.

       July 29 Mrs. Whistler and the two boys, James and William, returned to America, settled on a farm in Pomfret, Connecticut; the boys attended Christ Church Hall School.

1851   July 1. Entered West Point.

1854   June 16. Discharged from West Point for having over two hundred demerits as well as being deficient in chemistry. Did many drawings and was head of the art class.

       Apprenticed briefly with the Winans Locomotive works in Baltimore where his half-brother George was a partner.

       November 17. Began working for the U.S. Coast and Geodetic Survey in Washington. Learned etching technique.

1855   February 12. Resigned. Convinced his mother that he wanted to be an artist and study in Paris.

       October. With the assurance of a yearly allowance of $350, went to London to visit the Hadens and the following month to Paris.

1856   Enrolled in the *atelier* of Charles Gabriel Gleyre. As he had learned French in Russia, he could immediately join in the bohemian life of French students.

1858   Tour in northern France and Rhine. Published The Twelve Etchings from Nature usually called the "French Set." At the Louvre he met Fantin-Latour who introduced him to Courbet and other French artists.

1859 His first major painting, *At the Piano*, refused by the Salon.

May. Moved to London, visited Hadens, also had rooms in Wapping. Did many etchings of the Thames.

1860 *At the Piano* shown at the Royal Academy.

1861 In France, painted *The Coast of Brittany*, showing Courbet influence.

In Paris painted *The White Girl*, later called *Symphony in White, No. 1,* posed by Jo (Joanna Hiffernan) his red-headed Irish model and mistress.

1862 *The White Girl* rejected by the Royal Academy.

1863 *The White Girl* rejected by the Salon but shown at the Salon des Refusés where it was admired by artists. Took house with his mother at 7 Lindsey Row, Chelsea. Great interest in collecting blue-and-white porcelain and Japanese prints.

1864 Series of Oriental subject pictures of women in Chinese robes and also *The Little White Girl*, all showing Pre-Raphaelite influence.

1865 *The Little White Girl* shown at Royal Academy. Met Albert Moore whose classical subjects greatly influenced him for a time. His brother, Dr. William Whistler, came to live in London.

1866 Trip to Valparaiso, Chile. Moved to 2 Lindsey Row.

1867 Showed in American section of Exposition Universelle in Paris; greatly encouraged by Samuel P. Avery, his first American patron, to do more etchings.

1871 Published sixteen plates of the "Thames Set." Working on *Arrangement in Grey and Black, No. 1: Portrait of the Artist's Mother,* begun in 1867. Working on Nocturnes, formerly called Moonlights.

1872 Portrait of the Mother grudgingly accepted at Royal Academy. He never submitted there again, was never elected a member. Portrait of Thomas Carlyle. Musical titles much used from now on.

1873 Portraits of Mrs. Louis Huth, Miss Cicely Alexander and the Leylands. Started his famous Sunday breakfasts at noon, an innovation.

1874 First one-man exhibition at the Flemish Gallery, 48, Pall Mall. Maud Franklin replaces Jo as model and mistress.

1876   Peacock Room for Frederick Leyland's house in Prince's Gate.
       Artist's mother moved to Hastings for her health.

1877   Exhibition at the new Grosvenor Galleries opened by Sir Coutts Lindsay.
       The Falling Rocket aroused Ruskin's ire.

1878   E. W. Godwin built the White House for Whistler on Tite Street.
       Whistler sued Ruskin for libel, awarded a farthing's damages, was
       bankrupt and had to sell the White House.

1880   In Venice to do etchings for the Fine Arts Society. In December ex-
       hibited twelve etchings, the first Venice set, at the Fine Arts Society.

1881   Exhibited Venetian pastels.
       January 31, Mrs. Whistler died at Hastings.

1882   Portrait of Lady Archibald Campbell and two of Lady Meux. Walter
       Sickert became Whistler's pupil.

1883   Exhibition of Venetian etchings and a few other subjects at the Fine
       Arts Society.

1884   Visited Holland. Joined the Society of British Artists.

1885   Studio at 454A Fulham Road, lived in The Vale ("Pink Palace"),
       Chelsea.
       February 20. Delivered the Ten O'Clock lecture at Prince's Hall, Lon-
       don, expounding his aesthetic principles.

1886   Set of Twenty-Six Etchings issued by Dowdeswell.

1887   Took up lithography seriously, travelled in Belgium and Holland.

1888   Became intimate friend of French Symbolist poet, Stéphane Mallarmé.
       August 11. Married Mrs. Beatrix (Trixie) Godwin, widow of the
       architect E. W. Godwin

1889   Made Chevalier of the Légion d'Honneur.

1890   Moved to 21 Cheyne Walk. Published *The Gentle Art of Making
       Enemies.*

1891   Carlyle purchased by The Corporation of Glasgow and the portrait of
       his mother purchased for the Luxembourg. Made Officier of the Légion
       d'Honneur.

1892   The Whistlers moved to 110 rue du Bac, Paris.

1894   Sir William Eden commissioned small portrait of his wife; Whistler's dissatisfaction over payment led to legal proceedings.

1895   At Lyme Regis for wife's health.

1896   May 10. Trixie died of cancer at Hampstead.

1897   Boldini painted Whistler's portrait. Second Eden suit decided in Whistler's favor.

1898   Opened the Académie Carmen at 6 Passage Stanislas, Paris.

1899   Published *Eden versus Whistler: The Baronet and the Butterfly.*

1900   Dr. William Whistler died.

1901   Went to North Africa and Corsica for his health.

1902   Moved to 72 Cheyne Walk. Mrs. Birnie Philip (his mother-in-law) and her daughter Rosalind (whom he made his heir) came to look after him.

1903   July 17. Whistler died; buried at Chiswick Cemetery.

145

BIBLIOGRAPHY

Key to abbreviations for sources cited throughout the Catalogue:

Way and Dennis, 1903   Thomas R. Way and G. R. Dennis, *The Art of James McNeill Whistler. An Appreciation.* London, 1903.

Duret, 1904   Théodore Duret, *Histoire de J. Mc N. Whistler et de son Oeuvre.* Paris, 1904.

Cary, 1907   Elisabeth L. Cary, *The Works of James McNeill Whistler: A Study with a Tentative List of the Artist's Works.* New York, 1907.

Sickert, 1908   Bernhard Sickert, *Whistler.* London and New York, 1908.

Pennell, 1908   Elizabeth R. and Joseph Pennell, *The Life of James McNeill Whistler.* London and Philadelphia, 1908, 2 Vols.

Pennell, 1911   Elizabeth R. and Joseph Pennell, *The Life of James McNeill Whistler.* 5th ed., London and Philadelphia, 1911, 1 Vol.

Way, 1912   Thomas R. Way, *Memories of James McNeill Whistler, the Artist.* London and New York, 1912.

Gallatin, 1913   Albert E. Gallatin, *The Portraits and Caricatures of James McNeill Whistler. An Iconography.* London, New York, Toronto, 1913.

Gallatin, 1918   Albert E. Gallatin, *Portraits of Whistler, A Critical Study and Iconography.* New York and London, 1918.

Pennell, 1920   Elizabeth R. and Joseph Pennell, *The Life of James McNeill Whistler.* 6th ed., London and Philadelphia, 1920, 1 Vol.

Pennell, 1921   Elizabeth R. and Joseph Pennell, *The Whistler Journal.* Philadelphia, 1921.

Lane, 1942   James W. Lane, *Whistler.* New York, 1942.

Sweet, 1954   *Sargent, Whistler and Mary Cassatt.* (exhibition catalogue), Chicago and New York, 1954.

Young, 1960   Andrew McLaren Young, *James McNeill Whistler, an Exhibition of Paintings and Other Works, organized by the Arts Council of Great Britain and the English-Speaking Union of the United States.* (exhibition catalogue), London and New York, 1960.

Sutton, 1963   Denys Sutton, *Nocturne: The Art of James McNeill Whistler.* London, Country Life, 1963.

Drawings from the Clark Institute, 1964   Egbert Haverkamp-Begeman, Standish D. Lawder, and Charles W. Talbot, Jr., *Drawings from the Clark Institute; a Catalogue Raisonné of the Robert Sterling Clark Collection of European and American Drawings, Sixteenth through Nineteenth Centuries at the Sterling and Francine Clark Institute, Williamstown.* New Haven, Yale University Press, 1964, 2 Vols.

Sutton, 1966   Denys Sutton, *James McNeill Whistler. Paintings, Etchings, Pastels & Watercolours.* London, Phaidon Press, 1966.

Note: This bibliography includes works which have been used in the preparation of the catalogue, and does not pretend to be a complete list of the literature on the artist.

Key to abbreviations for sources cited throughout the Catalogue:

London 1881   *Venice Pastels. J. A. McN. Whistler.* Fine Arts Society, London, January, 1881.

New York 1889   *"Notes" — "Harmonies" — "Nocturnes."* H. Wunderlich & Co., New York, March 1889.

London 1892   *Nocturnes, Marines & Chevalet Pieces. J. McNeill Whistler, Chelsea.* Goupil Gallery, London, March-April, 1892.

Boston 1904   *Oil Paintings, Water Colors, Pastels, and Drawings. Memorial Exhibition of the Works of Mr. J. McNeill Whistler.* Copley Hall, Boston, February, 1904.

London 1905   *Memorial Exhibition of the Works of the late James McNeill Whistler.* New Gallery, Regent Street, London, 22 February - 15 April, 1905.

Paris 1905   *Exposition des Oeuvres de James McNeill Whistler.* Palais de l'Ecole des Beaux-Arts, Paris, May, 1905.

New York 1910   *Paintings in Oil and Pastel by James A. McNeill Whistler.* The Metropolitan Museum of Art, New York, 15 March - 31 May, 1910.

Buffalo 1911   *Oils, Water Colors, Pastels and Drawings. By James McNeill Whistler. Lent by Mr. Richard Canfield.* Buffalo Fine Arts Academy, Albright Art Gallery, 7 March - 27 April, 1911.

New York 1914   *Oils, Water Colors, Pastels & Drawings by James McNeill Whistler.* M. Knoedler & Co., New York, April, 1914.

12

23

Chicago 1917	*Exhibition of Whistleriana from the Collection of Walter S. Brewster,* The Caxton Club, Chicago, 28 April - 2 June, 1917.
Chicago 1923	*An Exhibition of Portraits of Whistler and Some Original Drawings by Whistler loaned by Walter S. Brewster.* The Arts Club of Chicago, 19 January - 7 February, 1923.
Chicago 1933	*A Century of Progress Exhibition of Paintings and Sculpture Lent from American Collections.* The Art Institute of Chicago, 1 June - 1 November, 1933.
Boston 1934	*Exhibition of Oils, Water-Colors, Drawings and Prints by James McNeill Whistler.* Museum of Fine Arts, Boston, 24 April - 13 May, 1934.
Chicago 1934	*A Century of Progress Exhibition of Paintings and Sculpture.* The Art Institute of Chicago, 1 June - 1 November, 1934.
New York 1938	*Whistler. Pastels & Water Colours.* Carroll Carstairs, New York, 12 January - 5 February, 1938.
New York 1942	*A History of American Watercolor Painting.* Whitney Museum of American Art, New York, 27 January - 25 February, 1942.
New York 1947	*Whistler. Loan Exhibition.* Macbeth Gallery, New York, 14 April - 10 May, 1947.
New London, Conn. 1949	*J. McNeill Whistler.* Lyman Allyn Museum, New London, Conn., 1 May - 13 June, 1949.
Chicago and New York 1954	*Sargent, Whistler and Mary Cassatt.* The Art Institute of Chicago, 14 January - 24 February, 1954, and The Metropolitan Museum of Art, New York, 25 March - 23 May, 1954.
London and New York 1960	*James McNeill Whistler, an Exhibition of Paintings and Other Works organized by the Arts Council of Great Britain and the English Speaking Union of the United States.* The Arts Council Gallery, London, 1-24 September, 1960, and The Knoedler Galleries, New York, 2-30 November, 1960.
Paris 1961	*Prélude à Whistler.* Centre Culturel Américain, Paris, 17 April - 10 June, 1961.

1

PAINTINGS

1 COAST OF BRITTANY — ALONE WITH THE TIDE.

Oil on canvas; 34¼ x 45½ in. Signed lower left: Whistler/1861.
Lent by the Wadsworth Atheneum, Hartford, Connecticut,
William Arnold Healy Fund.

Collections: George William Whistler, half-brother of the artist (purchased from him, late 1863) until 1869; Ross W. Whistler, George Whistler's son (owner in 1904); Ross Winans, George Whistler's son-in-law, Baltimore, Md., owner in 1905 (Sale, Christie's, London, 5 May, 1906, No. 103); P. and D. Colnaghi and Co., London (purchased at Winans Sale); Obach, London, 1909; Kraushaar Galleries, New York; Wadsworth Atheneum, purchased from Kraushaar Galleries, 1925.

Exhibitions: London, Royal Academy, 1862, No. 670; Boston 1904 (No. 42); London 1905 (No. 11); Boston 1934 (No. 7); Chicago 1934 (No. 420); New York 1947 (No. 12); New London, Conn. 1949 (No. 6); London and New York 1960 (No. 6).

Bibliography: Léonce Bénédite, *Gazette des Beaux-Arts*, XXXIII, 1905, pp. 498-499; Cary, 1907, No. 42 (and 494), also p. 162; Sickert, 1908, No. 5; Pennell, 1908, I, pp. 94, 96, 133, 312, repr. f. p. 94; *The Index of Twentieth Century Artists,* I, No. IX, June 1934, p. 143; Young, 1960, Cat. No. 6, repr. color pl. I; Sutton, 1963, p. 34, repr. color pl. I; Sutton, 1966, pp. 9, 186, repr. pl. 18 (color).

Whistler was in Brittany during the autumn of 1861, and this picture is the first of his major works to deal with the sea, a subject that he loved and painted repeatedly. When exhibited at the Royal Academy in 1862, it was called *Alone with the Tide,* a title later replaced by *Coast of Brittany.*

2 THE LAST OF OLD WESTMINSTER.

Oil on canvas; 24 x 30½ in. Signed lower left: Whistler 1862.
Lent by the Museum of Fine Arts, Boston.

Collections: John Cavafy, London, bought from Whistler soon after 1862; Dr. John Cavafy (John Cavafy's son); Edward S. Kennedy of Wunderlich & Co., New York (purchased from Dr. Cavafy, July 1892); Alfred Attmore Pope, Farmington, Conn., by 1898 (purchased from Edward Kennedy); Mrs. John W. Riddle (daughter of Alfred Pope), Farmington, Conn., by 1928; Museum of Fine Arts, Boston (purchased from Mrs. Riddle, 1939).

Exhibitions: London, Royal Academy, 1863, No. 352; Boston 1904 (No. 34); London 1905 (No. 35); Paris 1905 (No. 56); Boston 1934 (No. 6); Chicago 1934 (No. 426); New York 1947 (No. 7); London and New York 1960 (No. 7).

Bibliography: Cary, 1907, No. 34; Sickert, 1908, No. 11; Pennell, 1908, I, pp. 100-101, II, repr. f. p. 126; Way, 1912, repr. f. p. 82; *Connoisseur*, CXVII, 1946, pp. 45-46, repr.; Young, 1960, Cat. No. 7; Sutton, 1963, p. 41; Sutton, 1966, pp. 24, 186-187, repr. pl. 22.

Old Westminster Bridge stood for a century and when its stone arches began to give way a new iron bridge was constructed between 1854 and 1862. In Pennell (*loc. cit.*) is an account given by Arthur Severn of Whistler painting *The Last of Old Westminster* and from it we learn that the subject is not, as the title suggests, the dismantling of the old bridge (its piles are seen on the left) but the removing of the scaffolding of the new one. It was painted from the upper windows of Manchester building (now the site of Scotland Yard) overlooking the Thames.

3   THE WHITE GIRL: SYMPHONY IN WHITE, No. I.
Oil on canvas; 84½ x 42½ in. Signed upper right: Whistler 1862.
Lent by the National Gallery of Art, Washington, D. C.,
Harris Whittemore Collection.

Collections: the artist, 1862-?; Thomas Delano Whistler, Baltimore, Md., ?-1895; Boussod, Valadon & Co., New York, 1895-96; Harris Whittemore, Naugatuck, Conn. (purchased 1896), until 1897; John Howard Whittemore, Naugatuck, 1897 until his death, 1910; J. H. Whittemore Co., Naugatuck, 1910-43 (Miss Gertrude B. Whittemore had a life tenancy from 1910 until her death in 1941); given by Harris Whittemore Collection to National Gallery of Art, 1943.

Exhibitions: London, Berners Street Gallery, 1862, No. 42; Paris, *Salon des Refusés,* Palais des Champs Elysées, 1863, No. 596; Paris, *Exposition Universelle,* 1867, No. 68; London, *International Exhibition,* South Kensington Museum, 1872; Metropolitan Museum of Art, New York, July 1894-December 1895; Boston 1904 (No. 71); London 1905 (No. 37); Paris 1905 (No. 4); New York 1910 (No. 3); Boston 1934 (No. 4); Chicago 1934 (No. 433); Chicago and New York 1954 (No. 94).

Bibliography: Paul Mantz, *Gazette des Beaux-Arts,* per. 1, XV, 1863, pp. 60-61; Way and Dennis, 1903, pp. 21-22; Duret, 1904, pp. 20-22, repr. f. p. 18; Cary, 1907, No. 71, repr. f. p. 38; Sickert, 1908, No. 13, repr. frontispiece; Pennell, 1908, I, pp. 95-98, 102-103, 130, 140, 144, 146, 157, repr. f. p. 112; Pennell, 1920, pp. 67, 69, 70, 73-74, 100, 102, 110, 210, repr. f. p. 76; Pennell, 1921, pp. 4, 80, 161-163; *The Index of Twentieth Century Artists,* I, No. X, July 1934, p. 156, suppl. to Vol. I, Nos. IX and X, p. ii; Sweet, 1954, Cat. No. 94, repr. (color) pp. 80-81; Sutton, 1963, pp. 32-33, 36-38, 71, repr. fig. 6; Sutton, 1966, pp. 10, 37, 187, repr. pl. 25 (color).

Started in the winter of 1861, *The White Girl,* one of the most famous of Whistler's early paintings, was painted in Paris in his studio on the Boulevard des Batignolles. The model was Joanna Hiffernan (Mrs. Abbott) the copper-haired Irish girl, his mistress and principal model from 1860 to the early 1870's. Rejected in May by the Royal Academy of 1862, it was shown during that summer for the first time at the newly-opened Berners Street Gallery in London. Refused again by the Salon of 1863, it caused a sensation at the *Salon des Refusés* of 1863, where it eclipsed even Manet's *Le déjeuner sur l'herbe,* also in the exhibition. It was not until 1867 that Whistler used a musical title for a picture *(Symphony in White, No. 3)* and later, several others were renamed to fit into this nomenclature. He seems to have first applied "Symphony in White" to *The White Girl* in 1872 when he lent it to the International Exhibition, South Kensington. The frame, designed by the artist, includes the butterfly monogram on the right side above the center. Both the London 1905 and New York 1910 exhibition catalogues record differently an inscription, now no longer visible, in the artist's own hand on the back of the frame: *J. McN. Whistler, 2 Lindsay Houses, Chelsea* (London 1905)— *J. A. McNeill Whistler, 2 Lindsey Houses, Chelsea* (New York 1910).

4   GREY AND SILVER: BATTERSEA REACH.
Oil on canvas; 20 x 27⅛ in. Signed lower left: Whistler. 63.
Owned by The Art Institute of Chicago, Potter Palmer Collection.

3   *The White Girl: Symphony in White, No. 1.*
     Lent by the National Gallery of Art. Washington, D. C.,

43   *Mrs. Charles Whibley Reading.*
    Lent by the University of Glasgow

Collections: Mrs. Aglaia Coronio (sister of Whistler's friends Luke and Alecco Ionides), until 1892; Mrs. Potter Palmer, Chicago, bought from Mrs. Coronio, May 1892 (bequeathed to Art Institute, 1922).

Exhibitions: Royal Academy 1867 (No. 243); Goupil 1892 (No. 36); Boston 1904 (No. 70); Paris 1905 (No. 58); Chicago 1934 (No. 423); *Exhibition of American Painting,* M.H. De Young Memorial Museum, Palace of the Legion of Honor, San Francisco, Cal., 7 June - 7 July 1935, No. 242; Chicago and New York 1954 (No. 95); London and New York 1960 (No. 8).

Bibliography: Cary, 1907, No. 70; Sickert, 1908, No. 12 (and 105); Pennell, 1908, I, p. 144; Young, 1960, Cat. No. 8; Sutton, 1963, p. 42.

When first exhibited, at the Royal Academy in 1867, the picture was called simply *Battersea.* The present title is the one given to it for the Goupil retrospective exhibition of 1892, arranged by Whistler himself. At the time Whistler painted this river scene—a favorite view of his, which could well have been from his own windows—he was living in a house overlooking the Thames in Lindsey Row (now Cheyne Walk, Chelsea).

5 THE LITTLE WHITE GIRL: SYMPHONY IN WHITE, No. 2.

Oil on canvas; 30 x 20⅛ in. Signed upper right: Whistler. Date: 1864.
Lent by the Trustees of the Tate Gallery, London. (Shown only in Chicago)

Collections: remained unsold for some time; Gerald Potter, London, acquired before 1892; Arthur Haythorne Studd, bought from Goupil Gallery, London, late 1893 or early 1894; bequeathed by A. H. Studd to National Gallery of British Art (the Tate Gallery), 1919.

Exhibitions: London, Royal Academy, 1865, No. 530; London 1892 (No. 33); Paris, *Exposition Universelle,* 1900, (No. 76 in American section); Boston 1904 (No. 28); Paris 1905 (No. 5); New York 1910 (No. 6); Chicago and New York 1954 (No. 96); London and New York 1960 (No. 12); Paris 1961 (No. 2).

Bibliography: Léonce Bénédite, *Gazette des Beaux-Arts,* per 3, XXIV, 1900, p. 582; Duret, 1904, pp. 28, 30, repr. p. 32; Léonce Bénédite, *Gazette des Beaux-Arts,* XXXIV, 1905, pp. 152-153, repr.; Pennell, 1908, I, pp. 127-130, 144, 178, II, pp. 166, 251, 261-262, 280, repr. II, f. p. 252; Pennell, 1921, pp. 161, 191, 199, 200, 300; Martin Davies, *National Gallery Catalogues: The British School,* 1st ed., London, 1946, p. 171; Sweet, 1954, Cat. No. 96, repr. p. 84; Young, 1960, Cat. No. 12, repr. pl. 7; Sutton, 1963, pp. 39-41, repr. fig. 12; Sutton, 1966, pp. 13, 185, repr. frontispiece (color).

Joanna Hiffernan, the artist's Irish model and mistress, was the model for *The Little White Girl,* and the picture was the second of the series Whistler later called his "symphonies in white"—the musical title having been suggested perhaps by the expression ". . . *son sujet, qui n'est pas autre chose que la symphonie du blanc"* used by the critic Paul Mantz in 1863 to describe *The White Girl* (National Gallery of Art, Washington). *The Little White Girl* inspired Swinburne to write the poem *Before the Mirror: Verses under a picture,* which Whistler had printed on gold paper and fastened to the frame, and of which stanzas 4 and 6 appeared in the catalogue for the Royal Academy exhibition of 1865. The date "1864" in large numerals originally followed the signature, but Whistler painted it out in 1900.

6

6   PURPLE AND ROSE: THE LANGE LIJZEN OF THE SIX MARKS
(THE LANGE LEIZEN — OF THE SIX MARKS).
Oil on canvas; 36¼ x 24¼ in. Signed upper right in two cartouches:
Whistler 1864.
Lent by the John G. Johnson Collection, Philadelphia.

Collections: J. Leathart, Newcastle (purchased probably during the 1860's); John
G. Johnson, Philadelphia, 1893 (purchased from L. Leathart through Goupil
Gallery).

Exhibitions: London, Royal Academy, 1864, No. 53; London 1892 (No. 5); New
York 1910 (No. 4); Chicago 1934 (No. 425); New London, Conn. 1949 (No.
26); Chicago and New York 1954 (No. 99); London and New York 1960 (No.
11, shown in London only).

Bibliography: Anna M. Whistler, letter of 10 May, 1864 (printed in *Atlantic
Monthly*, CXXXVI, No. 3, September 1925, pp. 323-324); Léonce Bénédite,
Gazette des Beaux-Arts, XXXIV, 1905, pp. 146, 148; Cary, 1907, No. 492, also
pp. 57-58, repr. f. p. 56; Sickert, 1908, No. 15; Pennell, 1908, I, pp. 121-122, 127,
repr. f. p. 122; Pennell, 1920, pp. 87, 91, 306, 432, repr. f. p. 108; Sweet, 1954,
Cat. No. 99, repr. p. 87; Young, 1960, Cat. No. 11; Sutton, 1963, pp. 48, 50, 87,
repr. fig. 13; John Sandberg, *The Burlington Magazine*, CVI, November 1964,
pp. 503-504, repr. p. 502, fig. 28; Sutton, 1966, pp. 13-14, 187, repr. pl. 28.

This is probably the earliest of Whistler's many Japanese pictures and the title
refers to figures of elongated ladies on Chinese porcelain and to the potter's sign
of six marks. Despite the very unusual subject—a Victorian lady amidst a hetero-
geneous collection of Oriental accessories (all from Whistler's own collection)—the
composition is essentially that of a genre scene with a few exotic accessories and
it shows that Whistler had not yet begun to assimilate the lessons of Japanese
prints. The treatment of the figure reveals an affinity with Vermeer, whose name
was becoming known at that time in advanced French circles, and Corot's figure
pieces of the 1860's. The frame was especially designed for the picture and is
decorated with incised oriental motifs.

7

7 SEATED GIRL.
Oil on canvas; 10 x 16¼ in. Signed upper left: Whistler 1864.
Lent by Rita and Daniel Fraad, Scarsdale, New York.

Collections: James P. Gordon, New York (purchased from Hearn's Department Store Sale of paintings); Hirschl & Adler, New York.

Exhibition: American Painting. Selections from the Collection of Daniel and Rita Fraad, The Brooklyn Museum, 9 June - 20 September, 1964 and Addison Gallery of American Art, Phillips Academy, Andover, Mass., 10 October - 8 November, 1964, No. 10.

Bibliography: American Painting. Selections from the Collection of Daniel and Rita Fraad, (exhibition catalogue), Brooklyn, New York and Andover, Mass., 1964, No. 10, repr. p. 18.

In the Fraad Collection exhibition catalogue it is suggested that the model may be a daughter of Frederick R. Leyland—the Liverpool shipowner, art collector and patron of Whistler. This seems improbable because although Whistler and Leyland knew each other as early as 1864 (Leyland already was advancing him money then) it was not until the early 1870's that Whistler started to work on portraits of the various members of the Leyland family, and the dry-point portraits he did of the three Leyland daughters, Elinor, Fanny and Florence, in 1873, depict them in early girlhood.

8 SKETCH FOR ROSE AND SILVER: "LA PRINCESSE DU PAYS DE LA PORCELAINE."
Oil on paper board; 24-3/16 x 13-3/8 in. Date: c.1863-1865.
Lent by the Worcester Art Museum, Worcester, Massachusetts.

Collections: probably Charles Augustus Howell, London (posthumous Sale, Christie's, London, 15 November, 1890, No. 433); E. J. van Wisselingh, purchased from Dowdeswell Gallery, London, 1891; Prof. Fred Brown, London, purchased from van Wisselingh, 1893; David Croal Thomson, London, purchased from Prof. Brown; Thomas Agnew & Sons, Ltd., London, purchased from D. C. Thomson; Alexander Young, London, purchased from Agnew, 1899; Boussod, Valadon & Co., purchased from Alexander Young; Howard Young Galleries, New York (sold to a New York collector, 1919); Theodore T. Ellis, Worcester, Mass., acquired some time before his death, 1933; bequeathed to Worcester Art Museum by Mrs. Theodore T. Ellis, 1940.

Exhibitions: New York 1947 (No. 5); London and New York 1960 (No. 10).

Bibliography: Léonce Bénédite, *Gazette des Beaux-Arts,* XXXIV, 1905, p. 148; Sickert, 1908, pp. 17, 18; *American Art News,* XVII, March 22, 1919, p. 3, repr. C. H. Sawyer, *Worcester Art Museum Annual,* IV, 1941, pp. 43, 47, repr. fig. 2; Burns A. Stubbs, *The Whistler Peacock Room,* The Freer Gallery of Art, Washington, D. C., 1951, p. 19; Young, 1960, Cat. No. 10; Sutton, 1963, pp. 42, 48, 59; Sutton, 1966, p. 187, see No. 26.

The finished picture, *Rose and Silver: La Princesse du Pays de la Porcelaine,* is now in the Freer Gallery of Art, Washington, but formerly was owned by Whistler's patron Frederick R. Leyland and hung in the Peacock Room (see No. 27 in this exhibition) at Prince's Gate, London. It was completed only after innumerable sittings and first exhibited at the Paris Salon, 1865 (No. 2220). Although the picture is signed and dated "Whistler 1864—" there is evidence that it still was not finished by 1865, for in a letter he wrote Fantin-Latour that year (quoted in Bénédite, *loc. cit.*) Whistler mentioned that he was working night and day on the *Princesse*, the picture having been put aside until then on account of the model's ill health. The sitter for the Freer picture was Christine Spartali (later Countess Edmond de Cahen) whose father was, at the time, Greek Counsul General in London. The Worcester sketch, one of several preparatory versions, shows a different model, much more Japanese in appearance than the Pre-Raphaelite-featured Miss Spartali.

9

9   BATTERSEA REACH.
Oil on canvas; 20 x 30 in. Signed lower right: butterfly monogram.
Date: c.1863-1865.
Lent by the Corcoran Gallery of Art, Washington, D. C.,
Bequest of James Parmelee.

Collections: John Cavafy, London, purchased from Whistler; Dr. John Cavafy, London (son of John Cavafy); Edward G. Kennedy of Wunderlich & Co., New York (purchased from Dr. John Cavafy, July 1892); Isaac Cook, Jr., St. Louis, Mo., 1911; James Parmelee (bequeathed to Corcoran Gallery, 1941).

Exhibition: An Exhibition of Paintings owned in St. Louis, City Art Museum of St. Louis, 1911, No. 84.

Bibliography: Lane, 1942, repr. p. 60; Sutton, 1963, pp. 42, 63, repr. fig. 9; Sutton, 1966, p. 186, repr. pl. 21.

10

At the time *Battersea Reach* was painted Whistler lived in a house overlooking the Thames at 7 Lindsey Row (now 101 Cheyne Walk), Chelsea. In a letter of 17 August, 1893, now owned by the Corcoran Gallery, Whistler wrote: "The picture called 'Battersea Reach' was painted by me. I cannot remember exactly in which year, but when I was living in Lindsey Row, Chelsea. It was a view of the opposite bank of the river, from out my window on a brilliant autumn evening—and the painting is a favorite of mine. It was bought from me by Mr. Cavafy—and remained always in the family until sold by Dr. John Cavafy to Mr. E. G. Kennedy of New York."

10   BEACH AT SELSEY BILL.
Oil on canvas; 24 x 18¾ in. Date: c.1865.
Lent by New Britain Museum of American Art, New Britain, Connecticut.

Collection: purchased by New Britain Museum from Macbeth Gallery, New York, 1949.

Bibliography: see Pennell, 1921, p. 64.

The headland of Selsey Bill is in Sussex, situated between Chichester and Portsmouth. Charles Augustus Howell, whom Whistler befriended in the 1860's and who became his man of affairs (after having been employed by Dante G. Rossetti and been private secretary to Ruskin), owned several cottages at Selsey Bill. Pennell mentions that Howell had in his possession a painting of *Selsey Bill Sands* by Whistler, and that Whistler in fact stayed with Howell at Selsey Bill "where we know he made an etching and at least one water-colour."

11   BROWN AND SILVER: OLD BATTERSEA BRIDGE.
Oil on canvas, subsequently mounted on prestwood; 25 x 30 in. Date: c.1865.
Lent by Addison Gallery of American Art, Andover, Massachusetts.

Collections: Alexander Ionides, London, until 1890; his son, Alecco, who sold it, 1893-95; Sir Edmund Davis, until about 1928; Croal Thomson of Barbizon House, London, 1928; Thomas Agnew & Sons, Ltd., London, 1928; purchased by Cornelius N. Bliss, 1928; given by Cornelius N. Bliss to Addison Gallery of American Art, 1928.

Exhibitions: London, Royal Academy, 1865, No. 343; Paris, *Exposition Universelle,* 1867; London 1892 (No. 31); London 1905 (No. 17); New York 1947 (No. 11); New London, Conn. 1949 (No. 18); Chicago and New York 1954 (No. 100); London and New York 1960 (No. 9).

Bibliography: Cary, 1907, No. 378; Sickert, 1908, No. 22; Pennell, 1908, I, p. 129, II, repr. f. p. 120; Luke Ionides, "Memories, I: Whistler in the Latin Quarter," *The Transatlantic Review,* I, No. 1, 1924, p. 40; Lane, 1942, repr. p. 34; Sweet, 1954, Cat. No. 100, repr. p. 88; Young, 1960, Cat. No. 9; Sutton, 1966, p. 186, repr. pl. 20.

The picture was commissioned by Alexander Ionides, the Anglo-Greek merchant, collector of paintings and Hellenistic statuettes, and first exhibited at the Royal Academy in 1865. An X-ray photograph has revealed the beginnings of a self-portrait beneath the barge and water on the right.

12   GREY AND GREEN: THE SILVER SEA.
Oil on canvas; 20¼ x 30¼ in. Signed lower right: Whistler. Date: 1865.
Owned by The Art Institute of Chicago, Potter Palmer Collection.

Collection: Mrs. Potter Palmer, Chicago (bequeathed to Art Institute, 1922).

Exhibitions: Boston 1904 (No. 12); Paris 1905 (No. 63).

Bibliography: Cary, 1907, No. 12; Sickert, 1908, No. 20; Sutton, 1963, pp. 51-52.

It is likely that this was painted during the summer of 1865, in Trouville, where Whistler had gone to join Courbet, and where Daubigny and Monet were also living. The stay in Trouville had a decisive effect on Whistler's work; it led him to discover a new and fresh way of handling paint and to develop a freer and more evocative style.

13   THE SEA.
Oil on canvas; 20¾ x 37¾ in. Date: c. 1865.
Lent by the Montclair Art Museum, Montclair, New Jersey.

Collections: John Howard Whittemore, Naugatuck, Conn. (in his possession, 1904); Miss Gertrude B. Whittemore, Naugatuck, Conn.; Harris Whittemore, Naugatuck, Conn. (Sale, Parke-Bernet Galleries, New York, 19 May, 1948, No. 89); purchased by Montclair Art Museum, 1960.

Exhibitions: Boston 1904 (No. 69); Paris 1905 (No. 61); Boston 1934 (No. 19); Chicago 1934 (No. 430); National Gallery of Art, Washington, D.C., 1941-1948.

Bibliography: Cary, 1907, No. 69; Sickert, 1908, No. 148.

14   CREPUSCULE IN FLESH COLOR AND GREEN: VALPARAISO.
Oil on canvas; 22½ x 29¾ in. Signed lower left: Whistler. Valparaiso. 1866.
Lent by the Trustees of the Tate Gallery, London. (Shown only in Chicago)

Collections: Charles Augustus Howell, London, acquired probably in the 1860's (Sale, Christie's, London, 15 November, 1890, No. 434); W. Graham Robertson, London, acquired at Howell sale (gift to Tate Gallery, 1940).

Exhibitions: London, French Gallery, 1867; Paris, *Exposition Universelle*, 1867; Paris, *Salon du Champs-de-Mars*, 1891, No. 937; London 1892 (No. 13); London 1905 (No. 93); Paris 1905 (No. 59); *Tate Gallery Wartime Acquisitions*, National Gallery, London, 1942, No. 142; London and New York 1960 (No. 15).

Bibliography: Cary, 1907, No. 214; Sickert, 1908, No. 17; Pennell, 1908, I, pp. 135, 139-140, II, p. 226; Pennell, 1920, pp. 99-100; Pennell, 1921, p. 279; Young, 1960, Cat. No. 15, repr. pl. 6; Sutton, 1963, pp. 52-53, repr. fig. 15; Sutton, 1966, pp. 15, 188, repr. pl. 35.

From January to November 1866 Whistler was in South America—the reasons for this trip are still obscure—spending most of the time at Valparaiso in Chile which was then fighting a war of liberation with Spain. On this journey he produced, or at least conceived, about half-a-dozen seascapes. These works reveal an increasing preoccupation with fleeting effects of light and atmosphere and compositional devices of Oriental art, and thereby achieve significance as the direct ancestors of the London Nocturnes of the 1870's. The Tate Gallery picture was called at first *Twilight on the Ocean.* The present title is the one given to it in 1892 for the exhibition at Goupil's in London.

15   THE ARTIST IN HIS STUDIO (WHISTLER IN HIS STUDIO).
Oil on panel; 24¾ x 18¾ in. Signed lower right: butterfly monogram
in cartouche. Date: c.1867-1868.
Owned by The Art Institute of Chicago, Friends of American Art Collection.

Collections: Douglas Freshfield (in his possession, 1905); The Friends of American Art, purchased 1912 (presented to Art Institute, 1912).

Exhibitions: London 1905 (No. 13); Chicago 1933 (No. 488); Chicago and New York 1954 (No. 97).

Bibliography: Cary, 1907, No. 375; Sickert, 1908, No. 164; Pennell, 1908, I, pp. 184-185, repr. f. p. 184; Gallatin, 1913, No. 6, repr. between pp. 24-25; Gallatin, 1918, No. 6, repr. between pp. 32-33; Pennell, 1920, pp. 130-131; Sweet, 1954, Cat. No. 97, repr. p. 85; Young, 1960, see Cat. No. 18; Sutton, 1963, pp. 57-58; Sutton, 1966, pp. 22, 189, repr. pl. 45 (color).

In 1867-68 Whistler considered painting a large studio picture portraying himself, his models, and his friends Fantin-Latour and Albert Moore—a theme inspired perhaps by Fantin's *Homage à la vérité: le Toast* (1864) or Courbet's *l'Atelier* (1855). The final picture was never executed, but its appearance is set forth in two oil studies, one belonging to The Art Institute of Chicago, the other to the Municipal Gallery of Modern Art, Dublin, which show in addition to Whistler himself, Jo (the White Girl) and a model he called "la Japonaise." Both sketches were shown in the London Memorial exhibition of 1905.

16   TANAGRA.

Oil on canvas; 12½ x 6⅞ in. Signed lower right: butterfly monogram.
Date: c.1867-1870.
Lent by Randolph-Macon Woman's College, Lynchburg, Virginia.

Collections: Robert Woods Bliss, Washington, D. C.; purchased by Randolph-Macon, 1953.

Exhibition: London and New York 1960 (No. 22).

Bibliography: Young, 1960, Cat. No. 22; Mary Frances Williams, *Catalogue of the Collection of American Painting at Randolph-Macon Woman's College,* Lynchburg, Va., 1965, pp. 98-99, xiii, repr. p. 98.

At one time called *Lady with a Japanese Fan*, Andrew McLaren Young *(loc. cit.)* renamed it *Tanagra* after relating it to a red chalk drawing in Glasgow University to which Whistler had given this title. A very similarly posed woman holding a fan occurs on a photograph of a Greek terracotta statuette in Whistler's album of photographs of Tanagra figures (also in Glasgow University). Early in the 1860's Whistler developed an interest in Greek (or Tanagra) statuettes and during the period 1867-70, figures derived from these prototypes, often in conjunction with the figures in Japanese woodcuts, appeared repeatedly in his work, producing a blend of Japanese and Greek which Denys Sutton has termed appropriately "a sort of latter-day Hellenised Orientalism." (1966, p. 21.)

17   BATTERSEA REACH FROM LINDSEY HOUSES.

Oil on canvas; 19¾ x 29¾ in. Date: c.1871.
Lent by the University of Glasgow, Birnie Philip Bequest.

Collections: with Whistler at the time of his death (1903); bequeathed to Glasgow University by his executrix, Miss Rosalind Birnie Philip, 1958.

Exhibition: London and New York 1960 (No. 25).

Bibliography: Young, 1960, Cat. No. 25, repr. pl. 9.

This is rather closely related to a picture called *Variations in Violet and Green,* dated 1871 (private collection, U. S. A.), and both would seem to belong to a transitional period which foreshadows the Nocturnes and other Thames pictures of the 1870's.

18 PORTRAIT OF DR. WILLIAM McNEILL WHISTLER (PORTRAIT OF MY BROTHER).
Oil on panel; 17-3/16 x 3-11/16 in. Date: c.1871-1873.
Lent Anonymously.

Collections: Dr. William McNeill Whistler (gift of the artist), London, died 1900; Mrs. W. McNeill Whistler, his widow (sold between 1908 and 1911); Burton Mansfield, New Haven, Conn., purchased before 1911 (still in his possession, 1920); William T. Cresmer, Chicago; Mrs. Moses Wentworth, Chicago; Private Collection, Chicago.

Exhibitions: Boston 1904 (No. 103); *Loan Exhibition of Paintings in Oil, Water Color, and Pastel, from the Collection of Mr. Burton Mansfield, of New Haven, Connecticut,* Carnegie Institute, Pittsburgh, 1 August-30 December, 1911, No. 71.

Bibliography: Way and Dennis, 1903, p. 40, repr.; Cary, 1907, No. 446; Sickert, 1908, No. 56; Pennell, 1908, I, p. 133; Pennell, 1911, p. 94, repr. f. p. 128; see Way, 1912, pp. 60-62; Pennell, 1920, p. 95, repr. f. p. 125; Pennell, 1921, p. 113.

In April 1865 Whistler was joined in London by his younger brother William Gibbs McNeill Whistler (1836-1900), a surgeon taking part in the American Civil War, who had been sent to England by the Confederate Army. The Civil War ended while he was there. He decided to remain in England and later established a reputation as one of the leading throat specialists in London. Pennell *(loc. cit.)* relates the portrait of Dr. Whistler to that of *Luke Ionides* (Cyril Ionides collection, Sussex), painted in 1860-61. Andrew McLaren Young, however, considers this early date impossible because the sitter was then in America, and proposes instead a dating of 1871-73 on the basis of stylistic affinity with Whistler's *Self Portrait,* in the Detroit Institute of Arts. In the *Journal* Pennell (1921, p. 105) recounts Mrs. Leyland's (the wife of Frederick Leyland) impression of Dr. Whistler: "Mrs. Leyland thinks there could be no greater contrast than between Whistler and the Doctor. Whistler quick and alert, the Doctor slow and deliberate—he would take half an hour almost to write the simplest prescription; Whistler slight, the Doctor short and heavy."

19 STUDY FOR ARRANGEMENT IN GREY AND BLACK, No. 2: THOMAS CARLYLE.
Oil on canvas; 10 x 10⅞ in. Signed middle right: butterfly monogram.
Date: 1872.
Owned by The Art Institute of Chicago, Gift of Emily Crane Chadbourne.

Collection: Mrs. Emily Crane Chadbourne, Chicago (given to Art Institute, 1956).

Exhibition: Four Centuries of American Art, The Minneapolis Institute of Arts, Minneapolis, Minn., 27 November, 1963 - 19 January, 1964.

Bibliography: see Pennell, 1908, I, pp. 170-172, Pennell, 1920, pp. 119-121.

This is very likely a preliminary sketch for the large portrait of the Scots philosopher which is in the Art Gallery and Museum, Glasgow, and which was the first work of Whistler's to be bought by a public collection. Sittings started for the portrait in 1872 and were still in progress in July of the following year. A pen and ink sketch for the portrait is in the Fogg Art Museum, Harvard University, and an oil study of the head and shoulders is in Haverford College, Pennsylvania.

19

20 NOCTURNE IN BLACK AND GOLD: ENTRANCE TO SOUTHAMPTON WATER (NOCTURNE, SOUTHAMPTON WATERS).
Oil on canvas; 20 x 30 in. Signed lower right: butterfly monogram, and 1872 (1874?—date not clear).
Owned by The Art Institute of Chicago, The Stickney Fund.

Collections: Alfred Chapman (in his possession, 1892); purchased for the Art Institute, 5 February, 1900.

Exhibitions: London, Grosvenor Gallery, 1882, (or 1884); London 1892 (No. 20); London 1905 (No. 9); Chicago 1933 (No. 489).

Bibliography: Cary, 1907, No. 58; Sickert, 1908, No. 77; Pennell, 1908, I, p. 167, II, repr. f. p. 108; Pennell, 1920, pp. 218, 432; Sutton, 1966, p. 192, repr. pl. 83.

The painting is one of a numerous series of night pictures Whistler called Nocturnes. When it was shown at Goupil's in 1892, it was called *Nocturne, Blue and Gold, Southampton Water.*

21 HARMONY IN GREY AND GREEN: MISS CICELY ALEXANDER.
Oil on canvas; 75 x 40 in. Signed center left: butterfly monogram.
Date: 1872-1874.
Lent by the Trustees of The Tate Gallery, London. (Shown only in Chicago)

Collections: commissioned by the sitter's father, W. C. Alexander, Aubrey House, Kensington, London; bequeathed by W. C. Alexander to the Tate Gallery, 1932.

Exhibitions: Mr. Whistler's Exhibition, 48, Pall Mall, London, 1874, No. 5; London, Grosvenor Gallery, 1881, No. 113; Paris, Salon, 1884, No. 2454; London 1892 (No. 23); London 1905 (No. 32); Paris 1905 (No. 18).

Bibliography: Léonce Bénédite, *Gazette des Beaux-Arts,* XXXIV, 1905, pp. 242-243, repr. f. p. 242; Cary, 1907, No. 189, also pp. 77-78, 187-188, repr. f. p. 78; Sickert, 1908, No. 39; Pennell, 1908, I, pp. 171-175, repr. between pp. 172-173, II, pp. 116, 276; Pennell, 1921, p. 301; James Laver, *Whistler,* London, 1930, pp. 141-143, repr. between pp. 136-137; *The Index of Twentieth Century Artists,* I, No. IX, June 1934, p. 143; Martin Davies, *National Gallery Catalogues: The British School,* 2nd ed., London, 1959, pp. 104-105; Reginald Colby, *Country Life,* CXXXII, 2 August, 1962, pp. 260-261, repr.; Sutton, 1963, p. 73, repr. fig. 29; Sutton, 1966, pp. 36-37, 189-190, repr. pl. 56 (in color).

Cicely Henrietta Alexander (1864-1932) was the second daughter of William Cleverley Alexander, a patron of Whistler and a collector of blue-and-white porcelain. She married Bernard Spring-Rice in 1906. W. C. Alexander is stated to have commissioned Whistler to paint portraits of all four of his daughters. A portrait of the eldest, Agnes Mary (also in the Tate Gallery, London), was left unfinished, and the present picture, undertaken at Whistler's request, is the only other painted. Executed in some seventy sittings in 1873, it was exhibited at Whistler's first one-man show in 1874, and favorably mentioned in a review of the exhibition which appeared in the *Evening Standard* of 24 June, 1874: "The attitude of the maiden is delightful in its prompt action and girlish bearing." An oil sketch of the girl's head is in Mrs. Hampden Robb's possession, Beverly Farm, Mass., and a full length pastel for, or connected with, the picture, belongs to the Misses R. and J. Alexander, London.

22

22 ARRANGEMENT IN BLACK, No. 2: MRS. LOUIS HUTH.
Oil on canvas; 75 x 39 in. Signed lower left: butterfly monogram in cartouche.
Date: 1873.
Lent by the Right Honourable Viscount Cowdray, Midhurst, Sussex.

Collections: Louis Huth, husband of the sitter, purchased from Whistler, 1873;
executors of the Huth family, 1920.

Exhibitions: Mr. Whistler's Exhibition, 48, Pall Mall, London, 1874, No. 3; London 1905 (No. 53); *Panama-Pacific International Exposition*, San Francisco, Calif.,
1915, No. 276; London and New York 1960 (No. 32).

Bibliography: Duret, 1904, p. 113, repr. p. 111; Cary, 1907, No. 405; Sickert, 1908,
No. 41; Pennell, 1908, I, pp. 178-179, repr. f. p. 180; Pennell, 1920, p. 126, repr.
f. p. 180; Young, 1960, Cat. No. 32, repr. pl. 13; Sutton, 1963, p. 76.

Louis Huth, like Whistler, was an admirer of Velázquez, and Whistler's debt to
the Spanish painter is discernible in the conception of a tall figure emerging from
the shadows through a juxtaposition of blacks and grays, and in the placement of
a full-length figure in an upright narrow canvas. The portrait was exhibited at
Whistler's first one-man show, 48, Pall Mall, 1874. A pastel study for the portrait
in included in this exhibition (No. 53).

23 CREMORNE GARDENS, No. 2.
Oil on canvas; 27 x 52⅝ in. Date: c.1875.
Lent by the Metropolitan Museum of Art, New York, Kennedy Fund, 1912.

Collections: Thomas Way, purchased from auctioneers before sale of Whistler's
White House, 1879; T. R. Way, London, (inherited from his father, Thomas
Way); Arnold H. Hannay (purchased from T. R. Way); purchased by the
Metropolitan Museum, February-March 1912.

Exhibitions: London 1905 (No. 25); Chicago 1934 (No. 422); New London,
Conn. 1949 (No. 19); Chicago and New York 1954 (No. 107); London and
New York 1960 (No. 36, shown in New York only).

Bibliography: Way and Dennis, 1903, p. 61, repr. f. p. 60; Cary, 1907, No. 383,
also pp. 62-64; Sickert, 1908, No. 52; Pennell, 1908, I, p. 258, II, repr. f. p. 40;
Way, 1912, pp. 135-138; *Bulletin of the Metropolitan Museum of Art,* VII, No. 4,
April 1912, pp. 74-75, repr.; Gallatin, 1913, pp. 7-8; Gallatin, 1918, p. 10; Pennell,
1920, p. 187; Young, 1960, Cat. No. 36, repr. pl. 12; Sutton, 1963, p. 67, repr. fig.
27; Sutton, 1966, p. 191, repr. pl. 68.

Cremorne Gardens by the Thames in Chelsea was a popular resort in the manner
of Prater, or Tivoli Gardens, and Whistler, who was drawn particularly to the
effects of its artificial lights and firework displays, did a series of four pictures
depicting the activities at Cremorne (presently in the Fogg Museum, Harvard
University, the Metropolitan Museum of Art, New York, and the Freer Gallery
of Art, Washington) which were probably painted before 1877 when the Gardens
were closed. It seems that originally this picture contained portraits of Whistler
himself and Leyland, but that these apparently disappeared sometime after 1908,
when the picture was cleaned (see Way and Dennis, *loc. cit.,* and Pennell, 1920,
p. 187).

24   JAPANESE SCREEN (2 Sections). Back painted by Whistler.
Distemper (?) on brown paper or leather; each panel 70 x 30 in.
Date: presumbly painted in the mid-1870's.
Lent by the University of Glasgow, Birnie Philip Bequest.

Collections: with Whistler at the time of his death (1903); bequeathed to Glasgow University by his executrix, Miss Rosalind Birnie Philip, 1958.

Bibliography: The Studio, XXXIV, 1905, p. 223 (repr. in photograph by M. Dornac of Whistler in his studio); Pennell, 1908, I, p. 138; Pennell, 1920, p. 98; Pennell, 1921, p. 302, same photograph as above repr. between pp. 18-19.

This has never previously been exhibited. The photograph taken by M. Dornac (repr. cited above) shows Whistler seated on a sofa in his Paris studio with the screen behind him. In the account of the period covering the years 1866-72 in Whistler's life, Pennell (1908 and 1920) describes the house at No. 2 Lindsey Row (now 96 Cheyne Walk), Chelsea—in which Whistler lived from the end of 1866 until August 1878—and states that in the studio "was the big screen he painted for Leyland but kept for himself, with Battersea Bridge across the top, Chelsea Church beyond, and a great gold moon in the deep blue sky." Pennell, unfortunately, does not specify at which time the screen was painted. Andrew McLaren Young has suggested a date around 1875-77, partly on stylistic and subject matter and partly coeval with the Peacock Room decorations.

25   ARRANGEMENT IN YELLOW AND GREY: EFFIE DEANS.
Oil on canvas; 76⅜ x 36⅝ in. Signed lower right: butterfly monogram, and inscribed lower left: . . . she sunk her head upon her hand / and remained seemingly / unconscious as a statue / The Heart of Midlothian / Walter Scott.
Date: c.1876.
Lent by the Rijksmuseum, Amsterdam.

Collections: E. J. van Wisselingh, purchased from Dowdeswell Gallery, London, about 1888; Baron R. van Lynden, The Hague, by 1889 (purchased from van Wisselingh); bequeathed to Rijksmuseum by the Baron's widow, Baroness R. van Lynden, 1900.

Exhibitions: Edinburgh, *International Exhibition,* 1886, No. 1412; London and New York 1960 (No. 41); Paris 1961 (No. 5).

Bibliography: Cary, 1907, No. 497; Duret, 1904, repr. p. 157; Pennell, 1908, I, p. 201, II, pp. 88-89, repr. f. p. 88; Pennell, 1921, pp. 163, 245, 247; Young 1960, Cat. No. 41, repr. color pl. V; Sutton, 1963, p. 77; Sutton, 1966, pp. 191-192, repr. pl. 74.

This was first exhibited at Edinburgh, International Exhibition, 1886. Effie Deans is one of the leading characters of Walter Scott's historical novel, *The Heart of Midlothian,* and this picture is one of only three with a literary theme which Whistler painted. The other two are the unfinished *Annabel Lee* and *Ariel.* The *butterfly* and the inscription are not contemporaneous with the painting, but were added at Baron van Lynden's request, probably in 1889, when Whistler was in Holland. The model is apparently Maud Franklin, who became Whistler's mistress in the 1870's and sat for numerous paintings and etchings. She, like Jo, had splendid red hair.

25

26

26   HARMONY IN YELLOW AND GOLD: THE GOLD GIRL,
CONNIE GILCHRIST.
*Oil on canvas; 85¾ x 43⅛ in. Signed right center: butterfly monogram and in-
scribed upper left: Connie Gilchrist. Date: c.1876.*
Lent by the Metropolitan Museum of Art, New York,
Gift of George A. Hearn, 1911.

Collections: the artist, London (bankruptcy sale, Sotheby's, London, 12 February,
1880, No. 87); Mr. Wilkinson (purchased at bankruptcy sale); Henry Labouchere,
until 1904 (?); Carfax & Co., London; George A. Hearn, New York, purchased
May 1910.

37   *Coast Scene: Bathers.*
     The Art Institute of Chicago

33   *Arrangement in Black; The Lady in the Yellow Buskin.*
Lent by the Philadelphia Museum of Art

Exhibitions: London, Grosvenor Gallery, 1879 (No. 55); New York 1910 (not in catalogue); London and New York 1960 (No. 40).

Bibliography: Way and Dennis, 1903, p. 9; Cary, 1907, No. 490; Sickert, 1908, No. 69; Pennell, 1908, I, pp. 201-202, 218, 248, 259, repr. f. p. 258, II, p. 23; *Bulletin of the Metropolitan Museum of Art*, VI, No. 3, March 1911, p. 66, repr. p. 68; Way, 1912, p. 25; Pennell, 1921, pp. 183, 271; Lane, 1942, repr. p. 42; Young, 1960, Cat. No. 40, repr. pl. 10; Sutton, 1963, p. 77; Sutton, 1966, p. 191, repr. pl. 73.

This work is one of the rare portraits by Whistler showing a subject in animated movement. Constance Macdonald Gilchrist (1865-1946) was a popular dancer at the Gaiety Theatre in London in 1876, and Whistler has painted her as she appeared on the stage, dancing with a skipping rope. She achieved a reputation in light comedy and burlesque, had many admirers, among whom the most noted was Lord Lonsdale who bequeathed her a considerable fortune, much to the disgust of his widow. Subsequently the Duke of Beaufort became her friend and at her wedding in 1892 to the impoverished young Edmond Walter Fitz-Maurice, 7th Earl of Orkney, he gave the bride in marriage. The Countess of Orkney was survived by her husband and one child, Lady Mary Constance Hamilton Gosling.

27 PRELIMINARY CARTOON FOR HARMONY IN BLUE AND GOLD: THE PEACOCK ROOM.
Watercolor and gouache on paper laid on canvas; 6 feet 3 in. x 13 feet.
Date: 1876-1877.
Lent by the University of Glasgow.

Collection: with Whistler at the time of his death, 1903 (not included in original Birnie Philip inventory; later discovered in a dark corner and rescued).

Bibliography: the most reliable accounts of the *Peacock Room* decoration are the following: Pennell, 1908, I, pp. 202-209; James Laver, *Whistler*, New York, 1930, pp. 151-159; Burns A. Stubbs, *The Whistler Peacock Room*, The Freer Gallery of Art, Washington, D.C., 1951; Peter Ferriday, *The Architectural Review*, CXXV, No. 749, June 1959, pp. 407-414; Young, 1960, see Cat. No. 118.

The re-decoration of Frederick R. Leyland's dining room in his new house at 49 Prince's Gate, Kensington, came about when Whistler suggested that the color of the border of the carpet and the coloring of the flowers on the leather panelling would spoil the effect of *La Princesse du Pays de la Porcelaine* which Leyland proposed to hang over the mantelpiece. The carpet was altered and Whistler given permission to touch up the leather. He began work in mid-1876. Leyland, who was away in Liverpool, had left him in charge and soon, instead of minor readjustments Whistler carried out an elaborate scheme of peacock decorations, transforming the dining room into the *Peacock Room*, which was finished in February 1877. The whole room was gold and blue, there were peacocks on the shutters and two large peacocks in different postures on the wall at the south end facing the fireplace and the *Princesse*. The *Peacock Room* ruined the friendship between Whistler and Leyland, and led indirectly to Whistler's bankruptcy in 1879 with Leyland as his chief creditor. The *Peacock Room* was entirely dismantled in 1904, after being purchased by Charles Freer. It is now installed in the Freer Gallery of Art, Washington, substantially as it was in Leyland's house, and is probably the only surviving example of Whistler's work as an interior decorator. The full sized cartoon is a preliminary study for the south wall.

28 NOCTURNE: WESTMINSTER.
(NOCTURNE: WESTMINSTER PALACE.)
Oil on canvas; 12¼ x 20¼ in. Date: late 1870's.
Lent by the John G. Johnson Collection, Philadelphia.

Collections: Théodore Duret, Paris (Sale, Galerie Georges Petit, Paris, 19 March, 1894, No. 42); John J. Johnson, Philadelphia.

Exhibitions: Boston 1904 (No. 59); New York 1947 (No. 2); New London, Conn. 1949 (No. 27).

Bibliography: George Moore, *Modern Painting*, London, New York, Melbourne, 1893, pp. 22-23; Cary, 1907, No. 59, also pp. 65-66; Sickert, 1908, No. 124; Sutton, 1963, p. 66; Sutton, 1966, pp. 24, 192, repr. pl. 79.

This is one of Whistler's most unusual and revolutionary Nocturnes and, according to Denys Sutton, probably dates from the late 1870's. Whistler first called his paintings of the night "moonlights," and it was his friend and patron, Frederick Leyland, who proposed the term "nocturne" for them. The Nocturnes were not painted on the site, but from reliance on memory aided by rough drawings done while boating on the Thames. In the execution of these night pictures Whistler developed a special technique which corresponded exactly to his aims, so that the essence of a scene was captured and reproduced with strictly pictorial means.

29

44

29 PORTRAIT OF MRS. LEWIS JARVIS.

Oil on canvas: 25 x 16 in. Date: 1878 or 1879.
Lent by the Smith College Museum of Art.

Collections: Mrs. A. M. Jarvis (owner in 1905); purchased by Smith College Museum of Art, 18 April 1908.

Exhibitions: London 1905 (No. 65); *Inaugural Exhibition,* Memorial Art Gallery, Rochester, N.Y., 1913, No. 134; *Exhibition of Portraits,* National Design Center of Marina City, Chicago, 25 September - 15 October, 1964.

Bibliography: Way and Dennis, 1903, p. 50; Cary, 1907, No. 416; Sickert, 1908, No. 170; Way, 1912, p. 115; Lane, 1942, repr. p. 95.

Whistler left London for Venice in September 1879, and according to Way (*loc. cit.*) the portrait of Mrs. Jarvis was painted "just before he went to Venice." In describing the proceeding of Whistler's bankruptcy sale, which took place at Sotheby's, 12 February 1880, Pennell (1908, I, p. 259) enumerates the principal acquirers of pictures by Whistler, or art objects in his possession, and says that "the Japanese bath fell to Mr. Jarvis." This gentleman very likely was the husband of the sitter. (In the 1920 edition of the *Life* he is listed in the Index as "Lewis Jarvis," though still referred to in the text as "Mr. Jarvis.").

30 THE GOLD SCAB (THE CREDITOR)

Oil on canvas; 73 x 55 in. Signed upper right: butterfly monogram, and inscribed on music score: The / "Gold Scab." / Eruption / in / Frilthy Lucre. Date: 1879. Lent by the California Palace of the Legion of Honor, Through the courtesy of The Patrons of Art and Music, San Francisco.

Collections: the artist, London (bankruptcy sale, Sotheby, London, 12 February 1880, No. 88); Dowdeswell Gallery, London (acquired at Whistler sale); Captain Henry S. Hubbell, London (purchased from Dowdeswell Gallery); G. P. Jacomb-Hood, London (found in a Chelsea pawnshop); Theron C. Crawford, London; S. & G. Gump Company, San Francisco; Mrs. Alma B. Spreckels, San Francisco, purchased 1914 (presented to California Palace of the Legion of Honor, after 1960).

Exhibitions: London, Goupil Gallery (perhaps late 1890's); London and New York 1960 (No. 42).

Bibliography: Pennell, 1908, I, pp. 255-256, 259, repr. f. p. 250; Pennell, 1921, pp. 113, 326; Young, 1960, Cat. No. 42; Sutton, 1966, pp. 29, 198, repr. f. p. 24, fig. 15.

In 1879 Whistler went bankrupt, and by a strange irony Frederick Richards Leyland (1833-1892), a Liverpool shipowner who had been his friend and patron since the mid-1860's and whose dining room at Prince's Gate he transformed into the celebrated *Peacock Room* in 1876-77 turned out to be his chief creditor. In revenge Whistler painted three caricatures of Leyland, of which *The Gold Scab* is the only one that survives. Leyland is shown as a demoniacal peacock breaking out in scabs of gold sovereigns, playing the piano while seated on a white house (reference to Whistler's newly-built house in Tite Street, Chelsea, which he had been obliged to sell). The shirt frills worn by the demon, the money bags and the punning inscription, deride Leyland's money and his predilection for frilled shirts.

31 ARRANGEMENT IN BLACK, No. 5: LADY MEUX.
Oil on canvas; 76½ x 51¼ in. Signed lower left: butterfly monogram.
Date: 1881.
Lent by the Honolulu Academy of Arts, Hawaii. (Shown only in Chicago)

Collections: Commissioned by the sitter; Admiral Sir Hedworth Meux; Lady Charles Montagu, his widow, (owner in 1940); Ian Gilmour, London; Hirschl and Adler, New York; Honolulu Academy of Arts (purchased from Hirschl and Adler, 1967).

Exhibitions: Paris, Salon, 1882, No. 2687; Brussels, Société des XX, 1884; *British Painting Since Whistler,* National Gallery, London, 1940, No. 25; London and New York 1960 (No. 44).

Bibliography: Way and Dennis, 1903, pp. 9, 47; Duret, 1904, pp. 94-95, 99, repr. f. p. 152; Cary, 1907, No. 485; Sickert 1908, No. 75; Pennell, 1908, I, pp. 301, 308, repr. f. p. 308, II, p. 136; Way, 1912, pp. 64-66, 71, 137; Pennell, 1920, pp. 211-212, 217, 312; Pennell, 1921, repr. f. p. 3; cf. *The Frick Collection. An illustrated Catalogue of the Works of Art in the Collection of Henry Clay Frick,* Pittsburgh, 1949, I, pp. 10-11; Young, 1960, Cat. No. 44, repr. pl. 15.

Lady Meux caused some bewilderment among critics at the Salon of 1882 by being catalogued unexpectedly as "Portrait de M. Harry-Men." This portrait is the first of three which the artist painted of the wife of Henry B. Meux, of the well-known London firm of brewers, later Sir Henry Meux, in 1881. According to Pennell (1908, I, p. 301) Whistler was pleased with the portrait and spoke of it as his "beautiful Black Lady." A pen and ink study for the portrait is included in this exhibition (No. 85). Lady Meux (c.1856-1910), born Valerie Susie Langdon and married in 1878, was a woman of beauty, spirit and character; she once created a sensation by appearing at a meet of hounds mounted upon an elephant.

32 ARRANGEMENT IN PINK AND PURPLE.
Oil on panel; 12 x 9 in. Signed middle right in red: butterfly monogram.
Date: c.1881-1885.
Lent by the Cincinnati Art Museum, The John J. Emery Fund.

Collections: Jacques-Emile Blanche, Paris; Alphonse Kann, Paris; Thomas Agnew, London; James P. Labey, until 1920; purchased for Cincinnati Art Museum, 1920.

Exhibitions: New York 1947 (No. 31); Chicago and New York 1954 (No. 102); London and New York 1960 (No. 48); *The Whistlers, A Family Reunion,* Cincinnati Art Museum, 9-31 January, 1965, No. 2.

Bibliography: Lane, 1942, repr. p. 85; Sweet, 1954, Cat. No. 102, repr. p. 89; Young, 1960, Cat. No. 48, repr. pl. 15; Sutton, 1963, p. 104.

Heretofore believed to represent Maud Franklin. Andrew McLaren Young proposes that this is the picture *Scherzo, arrangement in pink, red, and purple* described by Jacques-Emile Blanche in *Portraits of a Lifetime,* London, 1937, p. 56, as the portrait of Olga Alberta Caracciolo, later Baroness de Meyer, which he bought from Whistler.

33 ARRANGEMENT IN BLACK: THE LADY IN THE YELLOW BUSKIN.
(LADY ARCHIBALD CAMPBELL).
Oil on canvas; 86 x 43½ in. Date: c.1883.
Lent by the Philadelphia Museum of Art, W. P. Wilstach Collection; by courtesy of the Commissioners of Fairmount Park.

Collections: owned by the artist, 1892; Alexander Reid, Glasgow (owner in 1893-1894); W. P. Wilstach Collection, Philadelphia (purchased by Mr. Wilstach from William Burrell, 30 November 1895).

Exhibitions: London, Grosvenor Gallery, 1884, No. 192; Paris, Salon, 1885, No. 2459; London 1892 (No. 41); *World's Columbian Exposition,* Chicago, 1893, Department of Fine Arts, Cat. No. 758; *Sixty-Third Annual Exhibition,* The Pennsylvania Academy of the Fine Arts, Philadelphia, 18 December, 1893 - 24 February, 1894, No. 35; London and New York 1960 (No. 45).

Bibliography: Duret, 1904, pp. 95-99, repr. p. 97; Léonce Bénédite, *Gazette des Beaux-Arts,* XXXIV, 1905, repr. p. 245; Cary, 1907, No. 486; Sickert, 1908, No. 81; Pennell, 1908, I, pp. 218, 305-306, repr. f. p. 305, II, pp. 88, 90-91, 116, 132, 298; Pennell, 1921, p. 4; Young, 1960, Cat. No. 45; Sutton, 1963, p. 101, repr. fig. 42; Sutton, 1966, pp. 37, 193-194, repr. pl. 93.

The early title for the picture was simply *Portrait of Lady Archibald Campbell.* In 1892, for the Goupil Exhibition, Whistler changed its title to *Arrangement in Black: La Dame au Brodequin Jaune,* in reference to the laced boot of the foot in movement. Lady Archibald, born Janey Sevilla Callander, married in 1869 Archibald Campbell, the second son of the eighth Duke of Argyll. She lived until 1923. A woman of considerable distinction and beauty, she was keenly interested in the arts. Whistler did a great many studies of her in different costumes and poses, and started two other large portraits of her, *The Grey Lady* and *The Lady in Court Dress.* These appear to have been destroyed before his death.

34 ARRANGEMENT IN BLACK, No. 8: MRS. ALEXANDER J. CASSATT. (PORTRAIT OF A LADY.)

Oil on canvas; 75¼ x 35¾ in. Signed lower right: butterfly monogram.
Date: 1883-1885.
Lent by Mrs. John B. Thayer, Rosemont, Pennsylvania.

Collections: Alexander J. Cassatt, Philadelphia, died 1906; executors of Mrs. Cassatt, 1921; Mrs. John B. Thayer, granddaughter of A. J. Cassatt.

Exhibitions: London, Royal Society of British Artists, 1885, No. 362; Boston 1904 (No. 45).

Bibliography: Cary, 1907, No. 45, also p. 83; Sickert, 1908, No. 85; Pennell, 1908, II, p. 57; Théodore Duret, *Histoire de J. Mc N. Whistler,* Paris, 1914, p. 83; Pennell, 1920, p. 257, repr. f. p. 344; Pennell, 1921, p. 134 (see also drawing repr. f. p. 136, which Pennell relates to *Mrs. Cassatt,* but is more likely for another portrait, now lost, of one of F. R. Leyland's daughters); *The American Magazine of Art,* XII, No. 9, September 1921, repr. p. 292; Frederick A. Sweet, *Miss Mary Cassatt, Impressionist from Pennsylvania,* University of Oklahoma Press, Norman, Okla., 1966, pp. 74-75, 82, 103, 107; Andrew Dempsey, *Apollo,* LXXXIII, No. 47, January 1966, p. 31, and see also fig. 1.

Mrs. Alexander Cassatt, *née* Lois Buchanan, was the wife of Mary Cassatt's brother Alexander, known as Aleck, whom she had married in 1868. The portrait, which Mr. Cassatt commissioned Whistler to paint during a visit he and his wife made to the artist's studio, 13 Tite Street, Chelsea, was begun in April 1883, and Mrs. Cassatt posed for several days wearing a riding habit. In October of that year, Mary Cassatt, who had been to Whistler's studio to check on whether he had finished the portrait, wrote to her brother Aleck: "It is a work of Art, and as young Sargent said to Mother this afternoon, 'It is a good thing to have a portrait by Whistler in the family'" (Sweet, *loc. cit.,* p. 82). The portrait still was not finished in the spring of 1885, and it was only after it had been shown at the Society of British Artists exhibition in Suffolk Street in the winter of 1885-86, that Whistler sent it to the Cassatts with a letter of apology and, to make up for the long delay, he included *A Chelsea Girl* (No. 36 in this exhibition) as a present. The frame is the original one designed by Whistler, with the butterfly in blue on gold on the right-hand side. A drawing made by Walter Richard Sickert of the portrait of Mrs. Cassatt while it was being exhibited in Suffolk Street, was reproduced in the *Pall Mall Gazette* of 8 December, 1885, and sarcastically commented upon by the columnist. (see Dempsey, *loc. cit.*).

35

31

35   ARRANGEMENT IN BLACK: PABLO DE SARASATE.
Oil on canvas; 85½ x 44 in. Signed right center: butterfly monogram.
Date: 1884.
Lent by the Museum of Art, Carnegie Institute, Pittsburgh.

Collection: bought from Whistler by the Carnegie Institute, 1896.

Exhibitions: London, Society of Royal British Artists, 1885, No. 350; Paris, Salon, 1886, No. 2450; Pittsburgh, Carnegie Institute, 1896, No. 303; Boston 1904 (No 53); London 1905 (No. 19); Paris 1905 (No. 20); New York 1910 (No. 29); London and New York 1960 (No. 47).

Bibliography: Way and Dennis, 1903, pp. 48-49; Cary, 1907, No. 53; Sickert, 1908, No. 84; Pennell, 1908, I, pp. 126, 178, II, pp. 2-4, 8-9, 56, 298, repr. f. p. 4; Way, 1912, p. 80; Pennell, 1921, p. 4; John O'Connor, Jr., *Carnegie Magazine,* March 1950, pp. 275, 282, repr. cover; Young, 1960, Cat. No. 47, repr. pl. 16; Sutton, 1963, pp. 78, 102-103, repr. fig. 43; Sutton, 1966, p. 194, repr. pl. 95.

Pablo de Sarasate (1844-1908), Spanish violinist and composer, was famous as a virtuoso performer. In this portrait, which was finished by July 1884, he is shown less than life-size, as he would appear when seen at a distance on a concert platform. The portrait was exhibited at the first International of the Carnegie Institute in 1896, and having been purchased by the Trustees before the close of the exhibition, it became one of the first Whistlers sold to a public gallery in the United States. The frame is the original one designed by the artist, with the butterfly monogram on the right-hand side.

36   A CHELSEA GIRL.
Oil on canvas; 65 x 35 in. Date: c.1884-1886.
Lent by the Children of Mr. and Mrs. William Potter Wear, Cecilton, Maryland.

Collections: Alexander J. Cassatt, Philadelphia, 1886, present from the artist.

Exhibitions: World's Columbian Exposition, Chicago, 1893, Department of Fine Arts, No. 744; Boston 1904 (No. 48); Chicago and New York 1954 (No. 118); London and New York 1960 (No. 51).

Bibliography: Cary, 1907, No. 48; Pennell, 1920, p. 257, repr. f. p. 416; Sweet, 1954, Cat. No. 118, repr. p. 99; Young, 1960, Cat. No. 51.

Alexander Cassatt was the brother of Mary Cassatt. Early in April 1883 he commissioned Whistler to paint the portrait of his wife (see No. 34 in this exhibition), and paid for it before he and his wife returned to the United States at the end of that month. Whistler seemingly unable to finish the portrait, did not deliver it until about three years later, and to compensate for the very long delay, he sent along the little *Chelsea Girl,* now belonging to the great-grandchildren of Alexander Cassatt.

37   COAST SCENE: BATHERS.
Oil on panel; 5 x 8½ in. Signed lower right: butterfly monogram. Date: c.1885.
Owned by The Art Institute of Chicago, The Walter S. Brewster Collection.

Collections: Possibly the artist's estate; P. and D. Colnaghi and Co., London, 1918; M. Knoedler & Company, New York, 1919; R. C. Vose, Boston, 1919; Chester H. Johnson Gallery, Chicago; Walter S. Brewster, Chicago (bought from Chester H. Johnson, 1926); given by Walter S. Brewster to Art Institute, 1933.

Exhibitions: A Collection of Paintings lent by Messrs. R. C. and N. M. Vose of Boston, The Fine Arts Academy, Albright Art Gallery, Buffalo, 8-31 January, 1921; Chicago 1934 (No. 421); London and New York 1960 (No. 52).

Bibliography: Young, 1960, Cat. No. 52, repr. color pl. VI.

Whistler's title for this painting is not known. Young *(loc. cit.)* relates this work to outdoor scenes painted by Whistler after his return from Venice in 1880, which were nearly all done on small panels the size of a cigar box and proposes that it may have been executed in Dieppe during the summer of 1885.

38   BLUE AND SILVER, DIEPPE.

Oil on panel; 4¾ x 8⅜ in. Signed lower right: butterfly monogram.
Date: c.1885.
Lent by the New Britain Museum of American Art, New Britain, Conn.

Collections: Mrs. George Putnam (owner in 1947); purchased by New Britain Museum from Macbeth Gallery, New York, 1948.

Exhibitions: New York 1947 (No. 27); New London, Conn. (No. 29).

39   THE GENERAL DEALER (OLD GENERAL DEALER).

Oil on panel; 4⅞ x 8½ in. Signed upper left: butterfly monogram, and lower right on steps: another form of butterfly monogram, partly obliterated. Date: late 1880's or early 1890's.
Lent by the Museum of Art, Rhode Island School of Design,
Providence, Rhode Island.

Collection: John James Cowan, Murrayfield, Edinburgh (bought probably in the early 1890's and owned by him until sometime between 1905 and 1914).

Exhibition: Edinburgh, Royal Scottish Academy, 1904, No. 308; London 1905 (No. 94); New York 1914 (No. 7); Boston 1934 (No. 9); New York 1947 (No. 25); New London, Conn. 1949 (No. 12); London and New York 1960 (No. 53).

Bibliography: Cary, 1907, No. 439; Sickert, 1908, No. 184; Pennell, 1908, II, repr. f. p. 16; Young, 1960, Cat. No. 53, repr. pl. 23.

During the late part of his career Whistler depicted in various media numerous houses and shops viewed directly from the front. These works were executed in many different settings, which are not easy to identify unless the original title is recorded. This little painting represents, according to Young *(loc. cit.)*, a shop in Chelsea.

40   SEASCAPE: VIOLET AND SILVER, THE DEEP SEA.

Oil on canvas; 19½ x 28¼ in. A piece of linen is tacked to the back of the stretcher with the following notation in an unknown hand, presumably copied from an inscription on the back of the original canvas now covered by relining: Violet & Silver. The Deep Sea. / Exhibited in the Salon of the Champ de Mars. 1894. / & bought in my studio, Paris in October of that year by / John A. Lynch of Chicago. / J. McNeill Whistler. Date: c.1892.
Owned by The Art Institute of Chicago, Gift of Clara Lynch.

Collections: John A. Lynch, Chicago (purchased from Whistler in Paris, October 1894); Clara Lynch, Chicago, widow of John A. Lynch (given to Art Institute, 1955).

Exhibitions: Paris, *Salon du Champs-de-Mars,* 1894, No. 1181; Boston 1904 (No. 33).

Bibliography: Cary, 1907, No. 33.

The Salon referred to above was an annual exhibition organized by the *Société Nationale des Beaux-Arts*—a society founded in 1890 by a group of artists who had seceded from the official and less liberal *Société des artistes français* (organizer of the yearly Salons)—which took place at the palais des Beaux-Arts on the Champs-de-Mars. This work, when it was shown there in 1894, bore the title *Violet et Argent—la mer profonde.*

41 ARRANGEMENT IN FLESH COLOR AND BROWN: PORTRAIT OF ARTHUR J. EDDY *(ARTHUR JEROME EDDY)*

Oil on canvas; 82¾ x 36¾ in. Signed middle right: butterfly monogram, and inscribed on back of canvas presumably in the artist's hand: "Arrangement in / Flesh colour & Brown./Portrait of Arthur J. Eddy."/of Chicago / butterfly monogram/ Painted in my Studio in / Paris. October. 1894. / J. McNeill Whistler.
Owned by The Art Institute of Chicago, Arthur Jerome Eddy Memorial Collection.

Collections: Arthur Jerome Eddy, Chicago (commissioned the artist in 1893) until 1920; Mrs. Arthur Jerome Eddy and Jerome O. Eddy, Chicago, his widow and son (given to Art Institute, 1931).

Exhibitions: Boston 1904 (No. 18); *Exhibition of Paintings from the Collection of the Late Arthur Jerome Eddy,* The Art Institute of Chicago, 19 September - 22 October, 1922, No. 66; Chicago and New York 1954 (No. 119).

Bibliography: Cary, 1907, No. 18; Pennell, 1908, II, p. 156; Pennell, 1920, p. 324; Pennell, 1921, repr. f. p. 240; *The Arthur Jerome Eddy Collection of Modern Paintings and Sculpture,* The Art Institute of Chicago, 1931, Cat. No. 19, repr. frontispiece; Sweet, 1954, Cat. No. 119, repr. p. 100; Sutton, 1963, p. 128; Sutton, 1966, p. 196, repr. pl. 122.

Arthur Jerome Eddy (1859-1920) prominent Chicago lawyer, writer, critic, sportsman and collector, was one of the first critics in America to recognize the importance of Whistler. He also wrote a searching book on the artist, which was published in 1904. When he commissioned the portrait, Eddy specified that it should be finished by a certain date. It was painted in 1894 in Whistler's studio in the rue Notre-Dame-des-Champs, Paris. Though completed on time, the picture was not sent to Chicago until the following year because Whistler continued to give it finishing touches. Eddy made purchases from the Armory Show of 1913 and was one of the first collectors of the work of Kandinsky (four of which are in the Art Institute).

42 RED AND BLACK: THE FAN: MRS. CHARLES WHIBLEY.
Oil on canvas; 73¾ x 35⅜ in. Date: 1894.
Lent by the University of Glasgow, Birnie Philip Bequest.

Collections: with Whistler at the time of his death (1903); bequeathed to Glasgow University by his executrix, Miss Rosalind Birnie Philip, 1958.

Exhibition: London and New York 1960 (No. 61).

Bibliography: Pennell, 1908, II, p. 158; Young, 1960, Cat. No. 61.

In 1894 Whistler, according to Pennell, was at work on three portraits of Mrs. Whibley—including this one—in his Paris studio on the rue Notre-Dame-des-

Champs. Mrs. Charles Whibley, born Ethel Birnie Philip, was Whistler's sister-in-law, and she acted as his secretary in the 1890's. It was from Whistler's house on the rue du Bac, in Paris, that she was married to Charles Whibley in 1895. After the marriage Rosalind Birnie Philip took her place in the household.

43   MRS. CHARLES WHIBLEY READING.
Oil on panel; 8⅜ x 5 in. Date: 1894.
Lent by the University of Glasgow, Birnie Philip Bequest.

Collections: with Whistler at the time of his death (1903); bequeathed to Glasgow University by his executrix, Miss Rosalind Birnie Philip, 1958.

Exhibition: London and New York 1960 (No. 60).

Bibliography: Young, 1960, Cat. No. 60, repr. color pl. VIII; Sutton, 1963, p. 129, repr. fig. 53; Sutton, 1966, pp. 42, 195, repr. pl. 114 (color).

This was painted in 1894 in the drawing room of Whistler's house in Paris, 110 rue du Bac. In his later years, Whistler painted a number of small-scale, intimate interiors of this kind, which, from the point of view of subject and size, may be related to the work of such French *intimistes* as Bonnard or Vuillard.

44   MADAME CAMILLE D'AVOUILLE.
Oil on canvas; 31¾ x 21 in. Date: c.1895.
Lent by the Addison Gallery of American Art, Andover, Massachusetts.

Collections: Mme. Camille d'Avouille, Paris; Alfred Strölin, Paris (bought from Mme d'Avouille); W. B. Patterson, Glasgow (purchased from Mr. Strolin); W. A. Coats, Gerguslie House, Paisley (bought from W. B. Patterson); M. Knoedler & Company, New York; William Macbeth, Inc., New York (on consignment from Knoedler, January 1929); Thomas Cochran (purchased from William Macbeth, 5 February, 1929).

Exhibitions: Exhibition of the Collection of the late W. A. Coats, Esq., Galleries of the Society of British Artists, London, 1927, No. 260; Boston 1934 (No. 20); *Exhibition of American Painting,* M. H. De Young Memorial Museum, Palace of the Legion of Honor, San Francisco, Cal., 7 June - 7 July, 1935, No. 239; Chicago and New York 1954 (No. 120).

Bibliography: Sweet, 1954, Cat. No. 120, repr. p. 101.

Formerly dated 1855-60, but believed now—on the basis of stylistic evidence and costume worn by the sitter—to have been painted no sooner than 1895, presumably in Paris, where Whistler had returned to live in 1892.

45   THE LITTLE ROSE OF LYME REGIS.
Oil on canvas; 20 x 12¼ in. Date: 1895.
Lent by the Museum of Fine Arts, Boston.

Collection: purchased by the Museum of Fine Arts, Boston, William Wilkins Warren Fund, 1896.

Exhibitions: Boston 1904 (No. 43); London 1905 (No. 26); Paris 1905 (No. 42); New York 1910 (No. 38); Boston 1934 (No. 25); New London, Conn. 1949 (No. 4).

46

Bibliography: Cary, 1907, No. 43, also pp. 79-80; Sickert, 1908, No. 109; Pennell, 1908, II, pp. 78, 166, 205, 207, 298, repr. f. p. 166; Way, 1912, pp. 114-115; *The Index of Twentieth Century Artists*, I, No. X, July 1934, p. 150; Sutton, 1963, p. 130; Sutton, 1966, pp. 46, 195, repr. pl. 112.

See No. 46. The model for this picture was probably Rosie Rendall (1887-1958), the daughter of G. J. Rendall, Mayor and Alderman of Lyme Regis. She married Ernest Aubrey Herridge of Bath, Somerset, in 1914, had one son, and lived in Exeter, Devon, until her death.

46   THE MASTER SMITH OF LYME REGIS
(THE BLACKSMITH OF LYME REGIS)
Oil on canvas; 20 x 12¼ in. Signed center right: butterfly monogram.
Date: 1895.
Lent by the Museum of Fine Arts, Boston.

Collection: purchased by the Museum of Fine Arts, Boston, William Wilkins Warren Fund, 1896.

Exhibitions: Pan American Exposition, Buffalo, 1901, No. 99; Boston 1904 (No. 36); London 1905 (No. 24); Paris 1905 (No. 27); New York 1910 (No. 37); Boston 1934 (No. 24); New York 1947 (No. 10); New London, Conn. 1949 (No. 5).

Bibliography: Cary, 1907, No. 36, also pp. 141-142; Sickert, 1908, No. 108; Pennell, 1908, II, pp. 78, 166, 176, 207, 276, 293, 298, repr. f. p. 170; Way, 1912, pp. 114-115; *The Connoisseur*, XCIII, No. 393, May 1934, pp. 334, 346, repr.; *The Index of Twentieth Century Artists*, I, No. X, July 1934, p. 145; Sutton, 1963, p. 130.

In the late summer of 1895 Whistler went with his wife, whose health was deteriorating, to Lyme Regis, Dorset, and there he painted this work and *The Little Rose of Lyme Regis* (see No. 45). During his stay at Lyme Regis Whistler underwent a sort of artistic crisis, the exact nature of which is not clear, but it seems that the artist believed he had surmounted the problems facing him and was on the brink of a new departure. These two portraits, though not strikingly dissimilar from his other works, reveal several notable differences: a smaller scale canvas, a livelier and richer handling of the paint, and a more spontaneous contact with the subject matter. The master smith of Lyme Regis, whose name apparently was Sam Govier, was born in 1855 and still living in 1934.

47   STUDY OF A YOUNG GIRL'S HEAD AND SHOULDERS.
(PORTRAIT OF A YOUNG GIRL).
Oil on panel; 5⅞ x 3¼ in. Date: mid-1890's.
Owned by The Art Institute of Chicago, The Walter S. Brewster Collection.

Collections: Baroness de Meyer, 1905; Mrs. Lewis Larned Coburn, Chicago; Walter S. Brewster, Chicago (given to Art Institute, 1933).

Exhibitions: London 1905 (No. 58); Chicago 1934 (No. 432).

Bibliography: Cary, 1907, No. 410; Sickert, 1908, No. 175.

During the last decade of his life, Whistler produced many studies and portraits of young girls, and the little panel may well belong to this period of the artist's work.

48   MISS ROSALIND BIRNIE PHILIP STANDING.
Oil on panel; 9¼ x 5½ in. Date: c.1897.
Lent by the University of Glasgow, Birnie Philip Bequest.

Collections: with Whistler at the time of his death (1903); bequeathed to Glasgow University by his executrix, Miss Rosalind Birnie Philip, 1958.

Exhibition: London and New York 1960 (No. 70).

Bibliography: Young, 1960, Cat. No. 70, repr. pl. 22.

This was painted in Paris, in the drawing room of Whistler's house, 110 rue du Bac.

49   GOLD AND BROWN: SELF PORTRAIT.
Oil on canvas; 37¾ x 20¼ in. Date: 1898.
Lent by the University of Glasgow, Birnie Philip Bequest.

Collections: With Whistler at the time of his death (1903); bequeathed to Glasgow University by his executrix, Miss Rosalind Birnie Philip, 1958.

Exhibitions: Paris, *Exposition Universelle*, 1900 (No. 108 in American section); London and New York 1960 (No. 72).

Bibliography: Cary, 1907, No. 527; Sickert, 1908, No. 121 (confused with the half-length self portrait now in the National Gallery of Art, Washington); Pennell, 1908, II, pp. 204, 251; Gallatin, 1913, p. 21, No. 8; Albert E. Gallatin, *Notes on Some Rare Portraits of Whistler*, New York and London, 1916, p. 5; Gallatin, 1918, p. 28, No. 8; Pennell, 1920, pp. 359, 397; Young, 1960, Cat. No. 72, repr. pl. 36; Sutton, 1963, p. 134; Sutton, 1966, p. 197, repr. pl. 124.

This striking portrait, based on Velázquez' *Pablo de Valladolid* in the Prado, of which Whistler owned a photograph, was seen by Pennell in May 1898 in Whistler's studio in the rue Notre-Dame-des-Champs, Paris. Pennell remarks that it was "far from successful" and that Whistler "had little pleasure in it." It seems that the portrait was rubbed down by Whistler, after the Paris exhibition of 1900, for the purpose of repainting, but that this work was never done.

50   LILLIE IN OUR ALLEY.
Oil on canvas; 20½ x 12½ in. Date: c.1898.
Lent by The National Gallery of Canada, Ottawa, Canada.

Collections: Miss Rosalind Birnie Philip; acquired by the National Gallery of Canada, 1946.

Exhibition: James Wilson Morrice, Montreal Museum of Fine Arts, 1965, No. 143.

Bibliography: see Pennell, 1908, II, pp. 205, 207, 224; Robert H. Hubbard, *The Art Quarterly*, X, 1947, p. 229; Robert H. Hubbard, *The National Gallery of Canada, Catalogue of Paintings and Sculpture*, Ottawa, 1962, II, p. 164, repr.
In his final years Whistler spent much energy painting young girls. This resulted in a series of oil sketches which, at their best, are direct and fresh, and express various moods of adolescence from which is not excluded at times an element of pathos. Among the various Soho children used by Whistler as models in his Fitzroy Street studio was a Lily Pamington, who appears in at least four portraits of the period 1896-1900 (see Young, 1960, Cat. No. 65, repr. pl. 65), and whose resemblance

to the girl portrayed in *Lillie in our Alley* is such that she seems likely to be the same person. The present picture was painted probably as a study for *Gold and Brown: Lillie in our Alley,* first exhibited in 1899 at the second exhibition of the International Society of Sculptors, Painters and Gravers, London, subsequently owned by John James Cowan, Edinburgh, and now in the Fogg Art Museum, Harvard University. In the French edition of the *Life,* published in Paris, 1913, Pennell mentions (p. 371) that the title *Lillie in our Alley* is an allusion to the popular English song "Sally in our Alley."

51   THE BLACK HAT: PORTRAIT OF MISS ROSALIND BIRNIE PHILIP.
Oil on canvas; 24½ x 18½ in. Date: 1902.
Lent by the University of Glasgow, Birnie Philip Bequest.

Collections: With Whistler at the time of his death (1903); bequeathed to Glasgow University by his executrix, Miss Rosalind Birnie Philip, 1958.

Exhibition: London and New York 1960 (No. 78).

Bibliography: Pennell, 1908, II, p. 279; Pennell, 1921, p. 77; Young, 1960, Cat. No. 78, repr. pl. 24.

Rosalind Birnie Philip was Whistler's youngest sister-in-law and, after his wife's death in May 1896, he adopted her as his ward. He changed his will and made her his heir, eventually canceling all former bequests and leaving everything to her. It is possible that this picture was begun in 1900—a description in Pennell's *Journal* (1921, p. 77) for 14th July, 1900, mentions Whistler at work on a portrait of Miss Philip "in hat and boa close round her throat" which fits this one. According to Young *(loc. cit.),* however, it was Miss Philip's recollection that the portrait was painted in Whistler's Fitzroy Street studio in 1902.

50   51

52 SPRING.
Pastel; 10⅞ x 6⅞ in. Signed lower left on oriental vase:
butterfly monogram. Date: c.1868-1873.
Lent by Mr. Gordon T. Beaham, Jr., Shawnee Mission, Kansas.

Collection: Colonel Frank J. Hecker, Detroit, grandfather of the present owner.

Exhibition: Boston 1904 (No. 134).

Bibliography: Cary, 1907, No. 131.

Colonel Frank J. Hecker (1846-1927) became intimately associated with Charles Lang Freer (Whistler's devoted patron) through their collaborative work in the railroading business. In Detroit, where they started the first railroad-car building shop in the Middle West, they lived in adjoining houses, Hecker having built for himself the first turreted and balustraded French château to be seen in that city. Colonel Hecker owned several works by Whistler, including *Harmony in Green and Rose: The Music Room*, which is now in the Freer Gallery of Art, Washington.

52   55

53   STUDY FOR ARRANGEMENT IN BLACK, No. 2: MRS. LOUIS HUTH.
Pastel; 9 x 4¾ in. Signed right center: butterfly monogram.
Date: probably 1872-1873.
Owned by The Art Institute of Chicago, The Walter S. Brewster Collection.

Collections: Robert Dunthorne, Liverpool and London; Albert Roullier, Chicago; Walter S. Brewster, Chicago (bought from Albert Roullier, 1927); given by Walter S. Brewster to Art Institute, 1933.

On the reverse of this pastel is a study of Mrs. Huth seen from the back. The actual portrait (see No. 22) was completed in 1873 and is one of Whistler's earliest, full length standing figures. Whistler made excessive demands on those who posed for him. Pennell relates (1908, I, p. 179) that almost daily during one summer Mrs. Huth, who was not strong, was made to stand for three hours without a rest. "He had some mercy, however, and at times a model stood for her gown." Another pastel study for the portrait of Mrs. Huth is in the Ashmolean Museum, Oxford (see Sutton, 1966, p. 192, and pl. 75).

54   CLOUDS AND SKY, VENICE.
Pastel on grey textured, woven paper; 5 x 8⅝ in. Date: 1879-1880.
Lent by the City Art Museum of Saint Louis, Gift of J. Lionberger Davis.

Collections: Thomas Way; J. Lionberger Davis, Saint Louis.

Exhibitions: New York 1947 (No. 43); Chicago and New York 1954 (No. 111); London and New York 1960 (No. 85).

Bibliography: Sweet, 1954, Cat. No. 111; Young, 1960, Cat. No. 85.

55   THE DOORWAY, VENICE.
Pastel and charcoal on gray-brown paper; 11⅞ x 8 in. Signed lower right: butterfly monogram. Date: 1879-1880.
Lent by the City Art Museum of Saint Louis, Gift of J. Lionberger Davis.

Collections: Richard A. Canfield, Providence, R.I., until 1914; M. Knoedler & Company, New York, 1914; Harris Whittemore, Naugatuck, Conn., purchased from Knoedler's, 1914 (Sale, Parke-Bernet Galleries, New York, 19 May, 1948, No. 62); J. Lionberger Davis, Saint Louis.

Exhibitions: Paris 1905 (No. 166); New York 1910 (No. 19); Buffalo 1911 (No. 23); New York 1914 (No. 25); New York 1938 (No. 10); Chicago and New York 1954 (No. 114).

Bibliography: Cary, 1907, No. 289, repr. f. p. 138; Sweet, 1954, Cat. No. 114, repr. p. 97.

Whistler's only visit to Venice lasted from September 1879 to November 1880, and during that time he produced chiefly pastels and etchings. His method was to draw with black chalk on brown paper. Color was put in as with mosaics or stained glass—usually a flat tint of pastel between the black lines.

56   A STREET. VENICE.
Pastel on brown paper; 10½ x 4¼ in. Date: 1879-1880.
Lent by Mr. Ira Spanierman, New York.

Collections: Richard A. Canfield, Providence, R.I., until 1914; M. Knoedler & Company, New York, 1914; Mrs. Diego Suarez, New York, 1932 (the former Mrs. E. Marshall Field); Thomas Agnew & Sons, Ltd., London.

Exhibitions: Paris 1905 (No. 161); New York 1910 (No. 22); Buffalo 1911 (No.

21); New York 1914 (No. 23); New York 1938 (No. 6); London and New York 1960 (No. 82).

Bibliography: Cary, 1907, No. 286; Young, 1960, Cat. No. 82, repr. pl. 30.

Fifty-three of the Venetian pastels were exhibited in London in 1881 at the Fine Arts Society. Andrew McLaren Young *(loc. cit.)* has suggested that this may have been No. 8 in the exhibition, *Gold and Brown: Little Calle in San Barnaba.*

57   NOTE IN FLESH COLOR: THE GIUDECCA. (VENICE).
Pastel on brown paper; 5 x 9 in. Signed on paper on back of frame: butterfly monogram, and inscribed in Whistler's hand: To Boehm whose Art is exquisite and whose sympathy is sufficient. Date: probably 1880.
Lent by Amherst College, Amherst, Massachusetts.

Collections: Sir Joseph Edgar Boehm, Queen's Gate, London, gift of the artist; Burton Mansfield, New Haven, Conn., purchased from P. and D. Colnaghi and Co., London, 1909 (Sale, American Art Association, Anderson Galleries, Inc., New York, 7 April 1933, No. 14); George D. Pratt (purchased at Burton Mansfield sale).

Exhibitions: London 1881 (No. 13); *Loan Exhibition of Paintings in Oil, Water Color, and Pastel, from the Collection of Mr. Burton Mansfield, of New Haven, Connecticut,* Carnegie Institute, Pittsburgh, 1 August - 30 December, 1911, No. 70; New York 1947 (No. 38); New London, Conn. 1949 (No. 47); London and New York 1960 (No. 81, shown in New York only).

Bibliography: Way, 1912, repr. (thumb-nail sketch) f. p. 52; Young, 1960, Cat. No. 81.

Sir Joseph Edgar Boehm achieved a reputation as the foremost sculptor of portraits during the Victorian era, and he executed a terracotta bust of Whistler in 1872. In the exhibition at the Fine Arts Society, London, 1881, this pastel, according to the *Daily Telegraph,* 5 November 1881, was given the place of honor on the south wall of the gallery.

58   THE BLUE GIRL.
Pastel on light brown paper; 10½ x 6¾ in. Signed center right: butterfly monogram. Date: c.1893.
Lent by Mrs. Diego Suarez, New York.

Collection: Madame Blanche Marchesi (owner in 1905); in Mrs. Diego Suarez's possession by 1938.

Exhibitions: London 1905 (No. 79); New York 1938 (No. 7); London and New York 1960 (No. 98, shown in New York only).

Bibliography: Cary, 1907, No. 429; Young 1960, Cat. No. 98.

In the 1890's Whistler intended to paint a series of large-scale pictures that would represent an *Eve,* an *Odalisque,* a *Bathsheba,* and a *Danaë.* They were never carried out but "suggestions for the paintings were in the little pastels of undraped or slightly draped figures for which he found the perfect model in London. . . These pastels are numerous. . . They are drawings on brown paper of girls dancing, posing with fans, bending over bowls, drinking tea, usually filmy draperies floating about them . . . they have the exquisiteness of little Tanagra figures. . ." (Pennell, 1908, II, p. 206). *The Blue Girl* very likely belongs to this group of pastel studies for the paintings. Madame Marchesi owned several works by Whistler, including *Belle à jour: bleu et violet* which is now in the Fogg Art Museum, Harvard University.

60

59   COASTAL SCENE.
Watercolor; 9¼ x 12¾ in. Signed lower left: butterfly monogram. Date: 1870's.
Lent by Rita and Daniel Fraad, Scarsdale, New York.

Collections: George C. Fortson, New York; Arthur A. Marshall, New York (father of Virginia Zabriskie); Zabriskie, New York; estate of Leo Gerngross, New York.

Exhibitions: American Painting. Selections from the Collection of Daniel and Rita Fraad, The Brooklyn Museum, 9 June - 20 September, 1954 and Addison Gallery of American Art, Phillips Academy, Andover, Mass., 10 October - 8 November, 1964, No. 11; *200 Years of Watercolor Painting in America,* The Metropolitan Museum of Art, New York, 8 December, 1966 - 29 January, 1967, No. 55.

Bibliography: American Painting. Selections from the Collection of Daniel and Rita Fraad (exhibition catalogue), Brooklyn, New York and Andover, Mass., 1964, No. 11, repr. p. 19.

60   LADY IN GREY.
Gouache; 10¾ x 4⅞ in. Signed lower right: butterfly monogram.
Date: c.1875-1880.
Lent by The Metropolitan Museum of Art, New York, Rogers Fund, 1906.

Exhibition: 200 Years of Watercolor Painting in America, The Metropolitan Museum of Art, New York, 8 December, 1966 - 29 January, 1967 (No. 56).

Bibliography: Cary, 1907, No. 510a; Sadakichi Hartmann, *The Whistler Book,* Boston, 1910, repr. f. p. 82; Stuart P. Feld, *Antiques,* XC, No. 6, December 1966, p. 841, repr.

This was the first American watercolor to be acquired by purchase by the Metropolitan Museum of Art.

61   VENETIAN ATMOSPHERE.
Gouache on pasteboard; 4-1/2 x 8-3/16 in. Date: c.1880.
Owned by The Art Institute of Chicago, The Walter S. Brewster Collection.

Collections: Dowdeswell Gallery, London; W. A. Coates, Paisley; Chester H. Johnson, Chicago; Walter S. Brewster, Chicago, 1927 (purchased from C. H. Johnson); given by Walter S. Brewster to Art Institute, 1933.

In 1879-80 Whistler spent fourteen months in Venice. The chief products of his stay were pastels and etchings. He also made a number of watercolors, reverting to a medium which he does not seem to have used since his earlier Paris days and which, from then on, he used with increasing frequency.

62   CHELSEA SHOP.
Watercolor on wove white paper; 5 x 8-5/16 in. Date: c.1881-1884.
Owned by The Art Institute of Chicago, The Walter S. Brewster Collection.

Collections: Petit-Didier; Marcel Guiot, Paris; Walter S. Brewster, Chicago, 1924 (purchased from Marcel Guiot); given by Walter S. Brewster to Art Institute, 1933.

Exhibitions: New York 1942 (No. 68); Chicago and New York 1954 (No. 113).

Bibliography: Sweet, 1954, Cat. No. 113, repr. p. 97.

Whistler began to use watercolor as one of his principal media in about 1882 and the first showing of watercolor in any quantity took place in 1884 at Dowdeswell's Gallery in a one-man exhibition of his oils, watercolors and pastels.

63   THE OPEN DOOR.
Watercolor on tan paper; 10 x 6½ in. (sight). Date: c.1881-1885.
Lent by Cornell University, Andrew Dickson White Museum of Art,
Gift of Mr. and Mrs. Louis V. Keeler.

Collection: given by Mr. and Mrs. Keeler to Cornell, 1960.

64   BEACH AT DIEPPE.
Watercolor; 8⅛ x 4⅞ in. Signed lower right and on back:
butterfly monogram. Date: c.1885-1895.
Lent by Mr. and Mrs. John Pierrepont, New York.

Whistler is known to have visited Dieppe in 1885 and again several times during the 1890's.

65   GREY AND SILVER: CHELSEA EMBANKMENT.
Watercolor; 5 x 8½ in. Signed middle right in red ink: butterfly monogram.
Date: c1885-1889.
Lent by the Sterling and Francine Clark Institute, Williamstown, Massachusetts.

Collections: H. Wunderlich & Co., New York, 1889; Alfred Corning Clark; Robert S. Clark.

Exhibition: New York 1889 (No. 6).

Bibliography: Pennell, 1921, repr. f. p. 116; *Drawings from the Clark Institute,* 1964, I, Cat. No. 357, II, repr. pl. 186.

This drawing shows the embankment above the Thames River at Chelsea not far from the Albert Bridge which can be seen in the background. It probably dates from the late 1880's—when Whistler had fully mastered the potentialities of watercolor and was using the medium frequently—certainly not later than 1889, since it was exhibited in March of that year at H. Wunderlich & Co., New York.

66   THE CONVALESCENT.
Watercolor; 9½ x 6¼ in. Signed lower left: butterfly monogram.
Date: c.1886.
Lent by Mr. Ronald Tree, New York.

Collections: Dr. Lennox Browne, London; Dr. John W. MacIntyre, Glasgow (bought in late 1890's); Ronald Tree (purchased from M. Knoedler & Company, New York, 1932).

Exhibitions: Glasgow, Fine Art Institute, 1889 (No. 538); London 1905 (No. 48); New York 1938 (No. 8); London and New York 1960 (No. 89, shown in New York only).

Bibliography: Cary, 1907, No. 400; Pennell, 1911, repr. f. p. 332; Young, 1960, Cat. No. 89.

The model is Maud Franklin, Whistler's mistress, who lived with him until shortly before his marriage in 1888 to Beatrix Goodwin. A closely related watercolor of the same model and setting, called *Girl Reading in Bed*, is in the Walters Art Gallery, Baltimore.

67 GREEN AND BLUE: THE FIELDS, LOCHES. (GREEN FIELDS AT LOCHES).

Watercolor on silk; 4⅞ x 8⅛ in. (sight).
Signed lower left: butterfly monogram. Date: 1888.
Lent by Cornell University, Andrew Dickson White Museum of Art,
Gift of Mr. and Mrs. Louis V. Keeler.

Collections: Howard Mansfield, New York (purchased from H. Wunderlich & Co., New York, March 1889); given by Mr. and Mrs. Keeler to Cornell, 1960.

Exhibitions: New York 1889 (No. 3); Boston 1904 (No. 92); New York 1938 (No. 20); New York 1942 (No. 69).

Bibliography: Cary, 1907, No. 89; Albert E. Gallatin, *American Water-Colourists,* New York, 1922, repr. pl. 2 (in color).

This was done in the summer of 1888 during Whistler's wedding trip to the Touraine, from which he brought back to London a few watercolors and "about thirty beautiful little plates of Tours and Loches and Bourges" (Pennell, 1908, II, p. 77). It was exhibited in New York in March of 1889 at H. Wunderlich & Co. and bought on the last day of the exhibition by Howard Mansfield, an American lawyer who became widely known as a collector in the field of Oriental art and prints. Mansfield wrote a *Descriptive Catalogue* of Whistler's etchings and drypoints, which was published in Chicago in 1909.

68 ROUEN.

Watercolor on cardboard; 8½ x 5 in. Signed center right: butterfly monogram.
Date: 1892-1894.
Lent by The University of Michigan Museum of Art, Ann Arbor, Michigan,
Bequest of Margaret Watson Parker.

Collections: Possibly Thomas Agnew & Sons, Ltd., London, 1903; Margaret Watson Parker (purchased from W. Scott & Sons, Montreal, 24 December, 1906); Dr. Walter R. Parker (life interest, 1936-1955); University of Michigan Museum of Art, 1955.

Bibliography: The Art Journal, 55, September 1903; repr. p. 266; Herbert Barrows, *Bulletin of The University of Michigan Museum of Art,* No. 7, April 1956, pp. 27, 28-29, repr. fig. 19.

While living in Paris, between 1892 and 1895, Whistler visited Normandy and Brittany, making lithographs at Rouen, Vitré, Paimpol and Lannion. The University of Glasgow owns a lithograph called *The Priest's House, Rouen,* which dates from 1894, and perhaps the watercolor also dates from this period. There is a possibility, however, that the watercolor depicts not Rouen, but a street in Paris, because when it was reproduced in *The Art Journal,* 1903, it was entitled *Rue Laffitte.*

69   SUNDAY AT DOMBURG *(SUNDAY MORNING, DOMBERG).*
Watercolor; 6 x 9¾ in. (sight). Date: 1900.
Lent by the Fogg Art Museum, Harvard University, Louise E. Bettens Fund.

Collections: M. Knoedler & Co., New York; Edward D. Bettens, son of Louise E. Bettens, purchased from M. Knoedler & Co. for the Fogg Art Museum; Fogg Art Museum, 1917.

Exhibitions: Boston 1934 (No. 34); New York 1942 (No. 74).

Bibliography: Edward D. Bettens, comp., *Painter and Patron*, New York, 1918, p. 26, repr. f. p. 22; Albert E. Gallatin, *American Water-Colourists*, New York, 1922, repr. pl. 3; Lane, 1942, repr. p. 63.

During the summer of 1900 Whistler spent a week at Domburg, a small seaside resort near Middleburg, on the coast of South Holland. Pennell relates that with its little red roofs and wide beach, Domburg seemed enchanting to Whistler, and he "made a few water-colours which he showed us afterwards in his studio" (1908, II, p. 258).

71

70   BLUE AND SILVER: MORNING, AJACCIO.
Watercolor on cardboard; 9⅞ x 5¾ in. Signed and inscribed, in artist's hand, on paper attached to wood backing: Blue & silver — / Morning. / Ajaccio./ butterfly monogram. Date: 1901.
Lent by The University of Michigan Museum of Art, Ann Arbor, Michigan, Bequest of Margaret Watson Parker.

Collections: Richard A. Canfield, Providence, R.I., acquired from the artist, until 1914; M. Knoedler & Company, New York (bought from Richard Canfield, 1914); Mrs. Margaret Watson Parker (purchased from Knoedler & Cie, New York, 4 May, 1914); Dr. Walter R. Parker (life interest, 1936-1955); University of Michigan Museum of Art, 13 May, 1955.

Exhibitions: Boston 1904 (No. 146); Buffalo 1911 (No. 15); New York 1914 (No. 17); London and New York 1960 (No. 104).

Bibliography: Cary, 1907, No. 143; Herbert Barrows, *Bulletin of The University of Michigan Museum of Art*, No. 7, April 1956, pp. 27, 29-31, repr. fig. 18; Young, 1960, Cat. No. 104.

Whistler was in Corsica from January to May 1901, and though far from well, continued to work on small paintings, watercolors and lithographs. On the back of this watercolor is a slight sketch of a building and trees.

71   THE GOSSIPS, AJACCIO.
Watercolor partly outlined with pen and ink on cardboard; 10¾ x 7 in. Inscribed in Whistler's hand on label on wooden backing: The Gossips, Ajaccio / butterfly monogram. Date: 1901.
Lent by the Albright-Knox Art Gallery, Buffalo, New York, Gift of A. Conger Goodyear.

Collections: Richard A. Canfield, Providence, R.I., until 1914; M. Knoedler & Company, New York, 1914 (bought from Richard Canfield); Mr. and Mrs. Anson C. Goodyear, Buffalo (owner in 1923); A. Conger Goodyear, Buffalo and New York (owner in 1938); given by A. Conger Goodyear to Albright-Knox Art Gallery, 1942.

Exhibitions: Boston 1904 (No. 110); Paris 1905 (No. 95); Buffalo 1911 (No. 7); New York 1914 (No. 10); New York 1938 (No. 9); New York 1942 (No. 71); London and New York 1960 (No. 103).

Bibliography: Cary, 1907, No. 107, repr. f. p. 132; Lane, 1942, repr. p. 40; *Paintings and Sculpture in the Permanent Collection*, The Buffalo Fine Arts Academy, Albright Art Gallery, Buffalo, 1949, p. 209, No. 163; Young, 1960, Cat. No. 103, repr. pl. 31.

Whistler had fallen ill in Marseilles on his return from North Africa, and following the advice of his doctor he crossed over to Corsica, and remained in Ajaccio from January to May 1901.

72 THE ADMIRATION OF THE FURLOUGHMEN.
Pen and ink; 4-13/16 x 4¼ in. Signed lower right: J. W., and inscribed below: The Admiration of the Furloughmen. Inscribed in pencil by a later hand: Whistler. Date: probably 1852.
Lent by the Library of Congress, Prints and Photographs Division, Washington, D.C.

Collection: Joseph and Elizabeth Pennell (presented to Library of Congress, 1917).

Exhibition: London and New York 1960 (No. 106, shown in London only).

Bibliography: Young, 1960, Cat. No. 106.

During the three years he spent at the United States Military Academy at West Point, from 1851 to 1854, Whistler did many quick sketches of cadet life, most of them humorous or satirical. Some were independent drawings; others were done in notebooks or textbooks. Nos. 73 and 74 also belong to this group of cadet drawings. Executed in the delicate style of much nineteenth-century American illustration, they indicate that Whistler at that time was a capable but undistinguished illustrator; they gave no hint of his future development.

73 MERIT ITS OWN REWARD.
Pen and ink; 6¾ x 5¾ in. Signed lower left: J. W., and inscribed below: Merit it's own reward / or / The best man leads the Squad. Inscribed in pencil by a later hand: J. McN. Whistler/1852.
Lent by the Library of Congress, Prints and Photographs Division, Washington, D.C.

Collection: Joseph and Elizabeth Pennell (presented to Library of Congress, 1917).

Exhibition: London and New York 1960 (No. 107, shown in London only).

Bibliography: Young, 1960, Cat. No. 107.

Comment: see No. 72.

74 POSITION OF A SOLDIER.
Pen and ink; 6-1/16 x 5⅛ in. Signed lower left: J. W., and inscribed below: Position of a Soldier: annihilation of the / Bowels. Inscribed in pencil by a later hand: J.Mc.N. Whistler/1852.
Lent by the Library of Congress, Prints and Photographs Division, Washington, D.C.

Collection: Joseph and Elizabeth Pennell (presented to Library of Congress, 1917).

Exhibition: London and New York 1960 (No. 108, shown in London only).

Bibliography: Young, 1960, Cat. No. 108.

Comment: see No. 72.

75 SCENE FROM BOHEMIAN LIFE.
Pen and ink; 9⅜ in. diameter (circular form). Signed lower right: J. Whistler. Date: c.1857-1858.
The Art Institute of Chicago, Gift of John G. O'Connell.

Collection: John G. O'Connell, given to Art Institute, 1956.

In October 1855 Whistler left America for France and, except for occasional visits elsewhere, lived in Paris from 1856 to 1859. Perhaps his own very bohemian existence in Paris, or a source such as Henri Murger's highly successful *Scènes de la vie de bohème* (dramatized as *La vie de bohème* in 1849) provided the subject matter for this drawing. There is no indication of the original title. An obviously related pen and ink drawing, also done on circular paper and signed "J. Whistler," is in the Freer Gallery of Art, Washington, (No. 06.104). It represents *An Artist in His Studio*.

76   LITTLE GIRL SEATED.

Pencil on grey paper; 7¼ x 4½ in. Signed lower right: Whistler 1859.
Lent by Amherst College, Amherst, Massachusetts.

Collection: purchased from Robert G. McIntyre (formerly of William Macbeth, Inc., New York), March 1956.

77   STUDY FOR WEARY.

Black chalk; 9⅝ x 6⅞ in. Signed lower right in black chalk: Whistler.
Date: 1863.
Lent by the Sterling and Francine Clark Art Institute, Williamstown, Mass.

Collections: Bernard Buchanan MacGeorge, Glasgow (in his possession, 1905); Martin Birnbaum, New York; Esther Slater Kerrigan, acquired from M. Birnbaum, 1927 (Sale, Parke-Bernet Galleries, New York, 8-10 January, 1942, No. 32); Scott and Fowles, New York; Robert S. Clark (purchased from Scott and Fowles, 1942).

Exhibitions: London 1905 (No. 183).

Bibliography: Cary, 1907, No. 341; Pennell, 1908, see I, p. 101; II, repr. f. p. 156; Pennell, 1920, see p. 73; repr. f. p. 105; *Drawings from the Clark Institute,* 1964, I, Cat. No. 355, II, repr. pl. 184.

This drawing was executed by Whistler in 1863 as a preliminary study for his dry-point *Weary*, generally thought to represent his Irish mistress Joanna Hiffernan. Another study for the dry-point, close to the print and probably executed after the Clark version, is in the Lessing J. Rosenwald Collection, National Gallery of Art, Washington.

78   STUDIES OF NUDES. (SKETCHES OF "TILLIE").

Black and brown crayon and white chalk on brown paper; 11¾ x 7¾ in. (sight).
Date: 1867 (?) or 1873 (?).
Lent by the Fogg Art Museum, Harvard University, Gift of Philip Hofer.

Collections: Laurence W. Hodson (Sale, Christie's, London, 25 June, 1906, No. 137); James Tregaskis, London (purchased at Hodson sale); given by Philip Hofer to Fogg Art Museum, 1929.

Exhibitions: London 1905 (No. 163); Boston 1934 (No. 46); *The American Line, 100 Years of Drawing*, Addison Gallery of American Art, Phillips Academy, Andover, Mass., 1959, No. 56.

Bibliography: Cary, 1907, No. 322; see Pennell, 1908, I, repr. f. p. 144; Lane, 1942, repr. p. 50; Bartlett H. Hayes, Jr., *American Drawings*, New York, 1965, repr. p. 72, pl. 40 (in color).

In Howard Mansfield's descriptive catalogue of Whistler's etchings and dry-points (Chicago, 1909) is listed a dry-point, M-116, entitled *Tillie*, which shows the nude figure of a young girl stooping toward the left, very similar to the central sketch on the Fogg drawing. Mansfield states that on the impression in the Avery Collection (New York Public Library) Whistler wrote "Tillie Gilchrist" and "1873" and explains that Tillie was a popular model at the time. Perhaps the Fogg drawing is related to the dry-point. It should be noted that Pennell *(loc. cit.)* reproduces the dry-point as a study for the *Six Projects*—(or *Six Schemes* as they were called originally). These were a group of oil sketches done for a projected but not completed decorative piece which was to be called *The Three Girls* or *Symphony in White, No. IV*, commissioned by Frederick Leyland, and on which Whistler was working during 1867-69.

79 LADY WITH FAN.

Black and white chalk on brown paper; 8¼ x 5⅛ in. Signed center right: butterfly monogram. Date: early 1870's.
Lent by The University of Michigan Museum of Art, Ann Arbor, Michigan, Bequest of Margaret Watson Parker.

Collections: Margaret Watson Parker (purchased from Obach & Co., London, 30 December, 1905); Dr. Walter R. Parker (life interest, 1936-1954); University of Michigan Museum of Art, 1954.

Bibliography: Herbert Barrows, *Bulletin of The University of Michigan Museum of Art*, No. 7, April 1956, pp. 27, 30-31, repr. fig. 20; *A Handbook of the Collections of The University of Michigan Museum of Art*, Ann Arbor, Mich., 1962, repr. No. 37.

80 STUDY FOR ARRANGEMENT IN BLACK AND BROWN: ROSA CORDER.

Pen and brown wash, on the letterhead of the Arts Club, Hanover Square, London; 7-1/16 x 4-7/16 in. Signed along right edge: à mon Elève Pellegrini, followed by butterfly monogram, and inscribed on reverse in Whistler's hand (beginning of a letter): Dear Mr. Williams. Date: 1870's.
Owned by The Art Institute of Chicago, The Walter S. Brewster Collection.

Collections: Carlo Pellegrini (?); Daniel H. Farr, 1922; Albert Roullier, Chicago; Walter S. Brewster, Chicago, 1922 (bought from Albert Roullier); given by Walter S. Brewster to Art Institute, 1933.

Exhibition: Chicago 1923 (No. 13).

Bibliography: see Pennell, 1921, p. 70.

The finished portrait, *Arrangement in Black and Brown: Rosa Corder*, dates from about 1876 and is in the Frick Collection, New York. The sitter, an intimate friend of Charles Augustus Howell who apparently commissioned the portrait, studied under Felix Moscheles and painted race horses. Another study in pen and ink, which was once in the collection of Alan S. Cole, is reproduced in Pennell (1908, I, f. p. 296). There exists also a pencil sketch in the Baltimore Museum of Art (from the Lucas Collection) which is reproduced in *International Studio*, LXXII, February 1921, p. CXI. Carlo Pelligrini, the dedicatee, was an Italian artist who came to England, and drew caricatures under the name of "Ape" for *Vanity Fair*. A portrait he did of Whistler is included in this exhibition (see No. 221).

81 THE PIANO.

Black crayon (litho crayon); 6⅞ x 4¾ in. Inscribed on reverse in ink presumably in Ernest G. Brown's hand: This drawing by J. Mc N. Whistler / was done in chalk as a study / for the dry-point "The Piano" / Ernest G. Brown.
Date: 1875 (?).
Owned by The Art Institute of Chicago, The Charles Deering Collection.

Bibliography: see Pennell, 1921, p. 116, and dry-point repr. f. p. 125.

As stated in the inscription on the reverse this is a study for the dry-point *The Piano* (Wedmore-117, Mansfield-119, Kennedy-141) which is dated 1875 and apparently represents Miss Tinnie Greaves. Alice (Tinnie) Greaves was the sister of Walter and Henry Greaves (see No. 216 in this exhibition), boat-builders and hirers in Chelsea whom Whistler had met in 1863 and who became his pupils. Ernest G. Brown, presumed writer of the inscription cited above, was an art dealer associated with the Fine Arts Society in 1879, and later with the Leicester Galleries, and it was through his intermediary that the Society commissioned Whistler to produce twelve etchings of Venice which resulted in Whistler's Venice sojourn of 1879-80. Whistler later painted the portrait of Brown's daughter, entitled *Rose and Gold: Pretty Nellie Brown.*

82 SKETCH FOR THE BLUE GIRL (MISS ELINOR LEYLAND)

Pen and brown ink; 7 x 4-3/16 in. Signed center right in brown ink: butterfly monogram, and center left in pencil: butterfly monogram, and inscribed in unknown 19th century hand on sheet of paper to which drawing is pasted: Miss Eleanor [sic] Leyland. "Babs". original sketch for a picture never completed, / and destroyed by Whistler in the early part of 1879. Date: c.1873-1879.
Owned by The Art Institute of Chicago, The Bryan Lathrop Collection.

Bibliography: see Way and Dennis, 1903, p. 46, Duret, 1904, p. 48, Pennell, 1908, I, pp. 176, 258, 303, Pennell, 1911, pp. 124, 186, 211-212, 428, Way, 1912, pp. 29-30, Pennell, 1920, pp. 124, 187, 214, 218, 432, and Pennell, 1921, p. 134.

In the early 1870's Whistler undertook to paint the portraits of Frederick R. Leyland, the Liverpool shipowner and art collector, and his wife, which were finished in 1873 and exhibited the following year (now owned by the Freer Gallery of Art, Washington and the Frick Collection, New York, respectively). During the same period Whistler also began work on at least four full-length studies for portraits of the three Leyland daughters, Fanny, Elinor and Florence; these portraits, however, were never completed. One study depicted a young girl in riding habit; a second, a young girl in long white dress; a third, was owned until recently by The Brooklyn Museum and represented Florence (also called "Baby Leyland"). A fourth, entitled *The Blue Girl* and portraying either Elinor or Florence (identified as "Florence" by Way and Dennis, Way, and Pennell in the two later editions of the *Life* and in the *Journal*, but called "Elinor" in the first edition) was destroyed and cut up by Whistler. Two fragments, which formed part of the background for this picture were disposed of at the time of Whistler's bankruptcy in 1879 and are now in the Freer Gallery of Art (called *Purple and Blue* and *Yellow and Blue*). The pen and ink drawing is closely related to a pastel and chalk drawing in the Freer Gallery of Art (No. 05.126) called *The Blue Girl*, and may well have been executed as a sketch for *The Blue Girl* that was destroyed by 1879. Whistler returned to the theme of a *Blue Girl* in 1882 in another portrait called *Scherzo in Blue: The Blue Girl* for which the model was Maud Waller. In this picture (repr. Pennell, 1911, f. p. 300) which was left unfinished and subsequently destroyed, the arrangement of the figure, the pose and the costume, virtually repeated the scheme outlined in the drawing and the pastel.

76

84

83 BATTERSEA BRIDGE.
Charcoal with touches of white chalk and gray watercolor on paper: 10⅝ x 14 in.
Signed lower right: butterfly monogram. Date: c.1878-1879.
Lent by the Albright-Knox Art Gallery, Buffalo, New York,
Gift of George F. Goodyear.

Collections: given by George F. Goodyear to Albright-Knox Art Gallery, 1958.

Exhibition: The Nineteenth Century: One Hundred Twenty-Five Master Drawings: a loan exhibition organized for the Solomon R. Guggenheim Museum, New York, by the University Gallery, University of Minnesota, Minneapolis, 1962, No. 124.

Bibliography: Gallery Notes, The Buffalo Fine Arts Academy, Albright Gallery, XXII, No. 1, May 1959, p. 24.

The drawing is closely related to Whistler's earliest lithographs, the series of river subjects in lithotint, such as *The Broad Bridge* (Way-8), *The Tall Bridge* (Way-9), and *Old Battersea Bridge* (Way-12), which he produced in 1878-79.

84 WOMAN WITH PARASOL.
Pen and brown ink, over sketch in pencil; 6-3/16 x 3-11/16 in.
Signed lower right in brown ink: butterfly monogram. Date: c.1880-1886.
Lent by the Sterling and Francine Clark Art Institute, Williamstown, Mass.

Collections: G. R. Halkett, London (owner in 1905); Mrs. G. R. Halkett (owner in 1915); Knoedler, London; Robert S. Clark (bought from Knoedler, 1939).

Exhibitions: London 1905 (No. 177); *Panama-Pacific International Exposition,* San Francisco, 1915, No. 321.

Bibliography: Cary, 1907, No. 336; Pennell, 1908, II, repr. p. 314; Young, 1960, see Cat. No. 21; *Drawings from the Clark Institute*, 1964, I, Cat. No. 356, II, repr. pl. 185.

Although the subject of this drawing is more characteristic of the years 1867-73, when the Japanese influence was most pronounced in Whistler, the manner of drawing and the form of the butterfly point to his style of 1880-90. This later dating is supported by evidence from Pennell who states that the drawing is after Whistler's painting *Harmony in Blue and Gold* (present whereabouts unknown) which was shown at the Royal British Artists exhibition of 1886.

85 STUDY FOR ARRANGEMENT IN BLACK, No. 5: LADY MEUX.
Pen and brown ink; 5⅛ x 3¾ in. Signed lower left: butterfly monogram.
Date: 1881.
Owned by The Art Institute of Chicago, The Walter S. Brewster Collection.

Collections: Albert Roullier, Chicago; Walter S. Brewster, Chicago, 1929 (bought from Albert Roullier); given by Walter S. Brewster to Art Institute, 1933.

This is a full length study for the first of three portraits of Lady Meux that Whistler painted in 1881, which is presently owned by the Honolulu Academy of Art (see No. 31). The second portrait, *Harmony in Pink and Grey: Lady Meux*, is in the Frick Collection, New York; the third, never completed and showing Lady Meux with furs and a muff, was destroyed.

Arranged according to the catalogue by Edward G. Kennedy, The Grolier Club of the City of New York, 1910. References are given by the letter K followed by the catalogue number. Measurements are given in inches and fractions of an inch. Height precedes width. These etchings are owned by The Institute of Chicago. Donors are indicated by the following initials:

CB	The Clarence Buckingham Collection	HP	Gift of Mrs. H. E. Perkins
CD	The Charles Deering Collection	HW	The Harold K. Warner Bequest
SF	Gift of Stanley Field	LW	Gift of Louise Cobb Walker
BL	The Byron Lathrop Collection	EW	The Ethel Wrenn Bequest

86   SKETCHES ON THE COAST
      SURVEY PLATE (Only State)
1854-55. K1, 5¼ x 9¾, BL

87   SKETCH ON ANACAPA ISLAND
      (Only State)
1854. K (Appendix I), 5¼ x 8¾, CB

88

88   FUMETTE (State IV)
1858, signed on plate: Whistler (lower right); inscribed on plate: Imp. Delatre. Rue St. Jacques. 171. (lower left); signed in margin: Whistler and Butterfly (lower left, in pencil). K13, 6⅜ x 4¼, BL

One of the Twelve Etchings from Nature (The French Set) published 1858.

89   EN PLEIN SOLEIL (State II)
1858, signed on plate: Whistler (lower left); inscribed on plate: Imp. Delatre. Rue St. Jacques. 171. (bottom right); signed in margin: Whistler and Butterfly (lower left). K15, 3⅞ x 5¼, BL

One of the Twelve Etchings from Nature (The French Set) published 1858.

90   THE UNSAFE TENEMENT
      (State III)
1858, signed on plate: Whistler (lower right); inscribed on plate: Imp. Delatre. Rue St. Jacques. 171. (lower left); signed in margin: Whistler and Butterfly (lower left, in pencil). K17, 6⅛ x 8¾, BL

One of the Twelve Etchings from Nature (The French Set) published 1858.

91   LA VIEILLE AUX LOQUES (State II)
1858, signed on plate: Whistler (lower right); inscribed on plate; Imp. Delatre, Rue St.

90

Jacques. 171. (lower right); signed in margin: Whistler and Butterfly (lower left, in pencil). K21, 8⅛ x 5¾, BL

One of the Twelve Etchings from Nature (The French Set) published 1858.

92 LA MARCHANDE DE MOUTARDE (State III)

1858, signed on plate: Whistler (lower left); inscribed on plate; Imp. Delatre, Rue St. Jacques. 171. (lower left); signed in margin: Whistler and Butterfly (lower left, in pencil). K22, 6⅛ x 3½, BL

One of the Twelve Etchings from Nature (The French Set) published 1858.

93 THE KITCHEN (State II)

1858, signed on plate; Whistler (lower right). K24, 8⅞ x 6⅛ inches, CB

One of the Twelve Etchings from Nature (The French Set) published 1858.

94 THE TITLE TO THE FRENCH SET (Only State)

1858, inscribed on plate: Imp. Delatre. Rue St. Jacques. 171. Nov. 1858 (upper left); inscribed on plate: Douze Eaux Fortes d'après Nature par James Whistler (upper right); inscribed on plate: a mon viel ami Seymour Haden (bottom, center); signed in margin: Whistler and Butterfly (lower left, in pencil). K25, 4⅜ x 5¾, BL

95 THE WINE-GLASS (State II)

Signed on plate: Whistler (lower left). K27, 3¼ x 2⅛, BL

96 ANNIE, SEATED (State II)

Signed on plate: Whistler (lower left); inscribed on plate: Annie (center, near bottom). K30, 5⅛ x 3¾, CD

97

97   READING BY LAMPLIGHT (State II)
Signed on plate: J. Whistler (lower right).
K32, 6-3/16 x 4-9/16, BL

98   THE MUSIC-ROOM (State I)
Seymour Haden (left), Charles L. Freer and
Mrs. Haden. K33, 5-11/16 x 8-5/16, CB

99   THE MUSIC-ROOM (State II)
K33, 5-11/16 x 8-5/16, BL

100   THAMES WAREHOUSES (State II)
Signed and dated on plate: Whistler, 1859 [?]
(lower right); signed in margin: Butterfly
(lower left, in pencil). K38, 3 x 8, BL

One of the Sixteen Etchings of the Thames Set,
published in 1871.

101   OLD WESTMINSTER BRIDGE
        (State II)
Signed and dated on plate: Whistler, 1859
(lower left); signed in margin: Butterfly (lower
left). K39, 2-7/8 x 7-15/16, BL

One of the Sixteen Etchings of the Thames Set,
published in 1871.

102   EAGLE WHARF (Only State)
Signed and dated on plate: Whistler, 1859
(center left); signed in margin: Butterfly (lower
right, in pencil). K41, 5⅜ x 8⅜, BL

One of the Sixteen Etchings of the Thames Set,
published in 1871.

103   BLACK LION WHARF (State III)
Signed and dated on plate: Whistler, 1859
(lower right); signed in margin: Butterfly
(lower right, in pencil). K42, 5⅞ x 8⅞, BL

One of the Sixteen Etchings of the Thames Set,
published in 1871.

104   THAMES POLICE (Wapping Wharf)
        (State II)
Signed and dated on plate: Whistler, 1859
(lower right); signed in margin: Butterfly
(lower left, in pencil). K44, 5⅞ x 8⅞, BL

One of the Sixteen Etchings of the Thames Set,
published in 1871.

105   LONGSHOREMEN (Only State)
Signed and dated on plate: Whistler, 1859
(lower right). K45, 5⅞ x 8¾, BL

106   THE LIME-BURNER (State I)
Signed and dated on plate: Whistler, 1859
(lower right); signed in margin: Whistler
(lower left). K46, 9⅞ x 6⅞, CD

One of the Sixteen Etchings of the Thames Set,
published in 1871.

107   BILLINGSGATE (State VII)
Signed and dated on plate: Whistler, 1859
(bottom), signed in margin: Butterfly (lower
left, in pencil); inscribed in margin: Billingsgate (bottom). K47, 5⅞ x 8⅞, BL

108   SOUPE À TROIS SOUS (Only State)
Signed on plate: Whistler (on wall). K49, 5⅞
x 8⅞, BL

109   BIBI VALENTIN (State II)
Signed and dated on plate: Whistler, 1859
(lower left). K50, 6 x 8⅞, CB

103

106

110   BIBI LALOUETTE (State II)
Signed and dated on plate: Whistler, 1859
(lower right). K51, 9 x 6, CB

111   BECQUET (The Fiddler) (State III)
K52, 10 x 7½, BL
One of the Sixteen Etchings of the Thames Set,
published in 1871.

112   SELF-PORTRAIT (State I)
Signed and dated on plate: Whistler, 1859
(lower right). K54, 8⅞ x 6, CB

113   FINETTE (State V)
Signed and dated on plate: Whistler, 1859
(lower right). K58, 11⅜ x 7⅞, CB

114   VENUS (State II)
Signed and dated on plate: Whistler, 1859
(lower left). K59, 6 x 9, CD

108

113

115

118

115 ARTHUR HADEN (State II)
Signed and dated on plate: Whistler, 1860 (lower left). K61, 8⅞ x 6, EW

116 ROTHERHITHE (State II)
Signed and dated on plate: Whistler, 1860 (lower left). K66, 10¾ x 7¾, HW

One of the Sixteen Etchings of the Thames Set, published in 1871.

117 OLD HUNGERFORD BRIDGE
(State III)
Signed on plate: Whistler (lower right); signed in margin (lower left, in pencil). K76, 5⅜ x 8⅜, BL

118 THE STORM (Only State)
Signed and dated on plate: Whistler, 1861 (lower right). K81, 6⅛ x 11¼, CB

119 ROSS WINANS (State I)
Signed on plate: Whistler (twice) (upper right); signed in margin (lower right, in pencil). K88, 9¾ x 7⅞, CB

120 WEARY (State II)
Signed and dated on plate: Whistler, 1863 (lower left); signed in margin: Butterfly with imp. (lower left, in pencil). K92, 7¾ x 5⅛, BL

121 SPEKE HALL, No. 1 (State VIII)
Signed, dated and inscribed on plate: Whistler, 1870, Speke Hall (lower right); signed on plate: Butterfly (left). K96, 8⅞ x 5⅞, CB

122 FLORENCE LEYLAND (State I)
Dry-point. Signed on plate: Butterfly (right); signed in margin: Butterfly with imp. (bottom, in pencil). K110, 8⅜ x 5⅜, EW

123 THE PIANO (State I)
Signed on plate: Butterfly (lower right). K141, 9⅛ x 6⅛, CB

124 ST. JAMES'S STREET (State I)
Signed in margin: Butterfly (lower right, in pencil). K169, 10⅞ x 6⅞, CB

125 "THE ADAM AND EVE," OLD
CHELSEA (State Ia)
K175, 6⅞ x 11⅞, SF

126 OLD BATTERSEA BRIDGE
(State IV)

Signed on plate: Butterfly (lower right); signed
in margin: Butterfly with imp. (lower left, in
pencil). K177, 7⅞ x 11⅝, EW

127 OLD PUTNEY BRIDGE (State III)

Signed on plate: Butterfly (bottom center);
signed in margin: Butterfly with imp. (lower
left, in pencil). K178, 7⅞ x 11¾, EW

128 LITTLE VENICE (Only State)

Signed on plate: Butterfly (lower left); signed
on tab: Butterfly with imp. (bottom, in pencil).
K183, 7¼ x 10⅜, CB

One of the Twelve Etchings, called The First
Venice Set, published in 1880.

129 NOCTURNE (State V)

Signed on tab: Butterfly with imp. (bottom, in
pencil). K184, 7⅞ x 11⅝, BL

One of the Twelve Etchings, called The First
Venice Set, published in 1880.

130 THE LITTLE LAGOON (State II)

Signed on plate: Butterfly (lower right); signed
on tab: Butterfly with imp. (bottom, in pencil).
K186, 8⅞ x 6, CB

One of the Twelve Etchings, called The First
Venice Set, published in 1880.

131 THE PALACES (State II)

Signed on plate: Butterfly (center left); signed
in margin: Butterfly with imp. (left, in pencil).
K187, 9⅞ x 14⅛, LW

One of the Twelve Etchings, called The First
Venice Set, published in 1880.

132 THE DOORWAY (State IIIa)

Signed on tab: Butterfly with imp. (bottom, in
pencil). K188, 11½ x 8, BL

One of the Twelve Etchings, called The First
Venice Set, published in 1880.

133 THE TRAGHETTO, No. 2 (State III)

Signed on plate: Butterfly (center left); signed
on tab: Butterfly with imp. (bottom, in pencil).
K191, 9¼ x 12, CB

One of the Twelve Etchings, called The First
Venice Set, published in 1880.

134 TWO DOORWAYS (State VI)

Signed on plate: Butterfly (upper left); signed
on tab: Butterfly with imp. (bottom, in pencil).
K193, 8 x 11½, BL

One of the Twelve Etchings, called The First
Venice Set, published in 1880.

135 THE BEGGARS (State III)

Signed on tab: Butterfly with imp. (bottom, in
pencil). K194, 12 x 8¼, BL

One of the Twelve Etchings, called The First
Venice Set, published in 1880.

136 SAN BIAGIO (State VI)

Signed on plate: Butterfly (center left); signed
on tab: Butterfly with imp. (bottom, in pencil).
K197, 8¼ x 12, BL

One of the Twenty-six Etchings published in
1886.

137 SAN GIORGIO (State II)

Signed on tab: Butterfly with imp. (bottom, in
pencil). K201, 8¼ x 12, SF

One of the Twenty-six Etchings published in
1886.

138 NOCTURNE: PALACES (State I)

Signed on tab: Butterfly with imp. (bottom, in
pencil). K202, 11⅝ x 7⅞, CB

One of the Twenty-six Etchings published in
1886.

139 UPRIGHT VENICE (State II)

Signed on plate: Butterfly (lower left); signed
on tab: Butterfly with imp. (bottom, in pencil).
K205, 10 x 7, HP

One of the Twenty-six Etchings published in
1886.

127

128

132

139

133

140 THE RIVA, No. 2 (State I)

Signed on tab: Butterfly with imp. (bottom, in pencil). K206, 8¼ x 12, CB

One of the Twenty-six Etchings published in 1886.

141 THE BALCONY (State IX)

Signed on plate: Butterfly (upper left); signed on tab: Butterfly with imp. (bottom, in pencil). K207, 11⅝ x 7⅞, CB

142 THE RIALTO (State I)

Signed on tab: Butterfly with imp. (bottom, in pencil). K211, 11½ x 7⅞, CD

One of the Twenty-six Etchings published in 1886.

143 LONG VENICE (State V)

Signed on plate: Butterfly (lower left); signed on tab: Butterfly with imp. (bottom, in pencil). K212, 5 x 12¼, BL

One of the Twenty-six Etchings published in 1886.

144 THE SMITHY (State III)

Signed on tab: Butterfly with imp. (bottom, in pencil). K240, 6⅞ x 8⅞, CB

145 THE FISH-SHOP, BUSY CHELSEA (State I)

Signed on tab: Butterfly with imp. (bottom, in pencil). K264, 5½ x 8½, CB

144

146 ROCHESTER ROW (State II)

Signed on tab: Butterfly (upper left); signed on tab: Butterfly (bottom, in pencil). K269, 5⅞ x 8⅞, CB

147 JUSTICE WALK, CHELSEA (State II)

Signed on tab: Butterfly with imp. (bottom, in pencil). K275, 6½ x 9½, BL

148 BIRD-CAGES, CHELSEA (Only State)

Signed on plate: Butterfly (upper left); signed on tab: Butterfly (bottom, in pencil). K276, 6 x 9, BL

149 CLOTHES-EXCHANGE, No. 2 (State II)

Signed on plate: Butterfly (center left); signed on tab: Butterfly with imp. (bottom, in pencil). K288, 9 x 5⅞, BL

150 MELON-SHOP, HOUNDSDITCH (State III)

Signed on plate: Butterfly (upper left); signed on tab: Butterfly (bottom, in pencil). K293, 5 x 7, BL

151 THE COCK AND THE PUMP (Only State)

Signed on plate: Butterfly (lower right); signed on tab: Butterfly with imp. (bottom, in pencil). K304, 8-11/16 x 5-1/2, CB

152 SALVATION ARMY, SANDWICH (Only State)

Signed on plate: Butterfly (lower right); signed on tab: (bottom, in pencil). K305, 3⅛ x 6⅞, CB

153 CAMEO, No. 1 (MOTHER AND CHILD) (Only State)

Signed on plate: Butterfly (center right); signed in margin: Butterfly (bottom, in pencil). K347, 6⅞ x 5, BL

154 COURTYARD, BRUSSELS (Only State)

Signed on plate: Butterfly (center right); signed on tab: Butterfly with imp. (bottom, in pencil). K355, 8½ x 5, CB

155 GOLD-HOUSE, BRUSSELS (Only State)

Signed on plate: Butterfly (center right); signed on tab: Butterfly (bottom, in pencil). K360, 7 x 2½, BL

156 PALACES, BRUSSELS (State I)

Signed on plate: Butterfly (left); signed on tab: Butterfly with imp. (bottom, in pencil). K361, 8⅝ x 5½, CB

157 GRAND' PLACE, BRUSSELS (Only State)

Signed on plate: Butterfly (center right); signed on tab: Butterfly (bottom, in pencil). K362, 8⅝ x 5½, CB

149

156

158   RUE DES BONS ENFANTS, TOURS
      (State III)

Signed on plate: Butterfly (center left); signed
on tab: Butterfly (bottom, in pencil). K372,
5⅞ x 3⅛, BL

159   LITTLE MARKET-PLACE, TOURS
      (Only State)

Signed on plate: Butterfly (center right); signed
on tab: Butterfly (bottom, in pencil). K375,
5 x 7, BL

160   CHANCELLERIE, LOCHES (State III)

Signed on plate: Butterfly (right center); signed
on tab: Butterfly with imp. (bottom, in pencil).
K383, 10½ x 6½, EW

161   CLOCK-TOWER, AMBOISE
      (Only State)

Signed on plate: Butterfly (lower left); signed
on tab: Butterfly (bottom, in pencil). K394,
7 x 5, BL

162   HÔTEL LALLEMENT, BOURGES
      (State I)

Signed on plate: Butterfly (left center); signed on tab: Butterfly with imp. (bottom, in pencil). K399, 6½ x 10⅝, CB

163   SQUARE HOUSE, AMSTERDAM
      (State II)

Signed on plate: Butterfly (upper right); signed on tab: Butterfly (bottom, in pencil). K404, 9 x 6⅞, BL

164   PIERROT (State V)

Signed on plate: Butterfly (upper left); signed on tab: Butterfly (bottom, in pencil). K407, 9 x 6¼, CB

165   THE EMBROIDERED CURTAIN
      (State III)

Signed on plate: Butterfly (upper left); signed on tab: Butterfly with imp. (bottom, in pencil). K410, 9⅜ x 6¼, EW

166   CHURCH, AMSTERDAM
      (Only State)

Signed on plate: Butterfly (lower left); signed on tab: Butterfly with imp. (bottom, in pencil). K411, 8⅝ x 5⅛, BL

167   ZAANDAM (State II)

Signed on plate: Butterfly (upper left); signed on tab: Butterfly (bottom, in pencil). K416, 5⅛ x 8⅝, BL

168   SUNFLOWERS, RUE DES
      BEAUX-ARTS (State I)

Signed on tab: Butterfly with imp. (bottom, in pencil). K422, 8⅝ x 11, BL

169   BOULEVARD POISSONIÈRE
      (Only State)

Signed on tab: Butterfly (bottom, in pencil). K423, 6⅛ x 9, BL

170   PANTHEON, LUXEMBOURG
      GARDENS (Only State)

Signed on plate: Butterfly (center right); signed on tab: Butterfly (bottom, in pencil). K429, 3¼ x 7⅞, HP

165

Arranged according to the catalogue by Thomas R. Way, Kennedy & Co., No. 613 Fifth Avenue, New York, 1914. Measurements are given in inches and fractions of an inch. Height precedes width. The numbers of proofs mentioned are those recorded by Thomas Way as having been printed by him.

All the lithographs listed below are owned by The Art Institute of Chicago, and unless otherwise indicated are part of The Bryan Lathrop Collection.

---

171   UNITED STATES MILITARY ACADEMY SONG OF THE GRADUATES.
(Cover of Sheet Music) 13⅜ x 10¼ in. Date: 1852.
Owned by The Art Institute of Chicago, The Walter S. Brewster Collection.

Collection: Walter S. Brewster, Chicago (bought from E. Weyhe, New York, April 1931) given by Walter S. Brewster to the Art Institute in 1933.

Bibliography: "Quarterly Notes," *Artwork,* VII, No. 26, Summer 1931, p. 84, repr. p. 85; John Sandberg, "Whistler's Early Work in America, 1834-1855," *The Art Quarterly,* XXIX, No. 1, 1966, pp. 51-52, 58, note 11, and p. 50, fig. 4 (reproduces impresson in collection of West Point, United States Military Academy.

Whistler made the cover drawing for the sheet music of the *Song of the Graduates* while he was a cadet at West Point, and it was lithographed by Sarony & Major, New York. It is undoubtedly the most ambitious of his West Point efforts and is described by Sandberg *(loc. cit.)* as a "finished, polished version of his West Point sketching style." Mr. Sandberg also publishes a letter (in the Birnie-Philip Collection, Glasgow University) written to Whistler in 1888, by J. L. Black, a former classmate: "I have today but one of your pieces. . . . It was lithographed as a frontispiece to a cadet class song and if my memory serves me right was drawn by you in my room—one of the figures was (little Aleck) E. P. Alexander, who became famous in the War of Rebellion and is now president of an extensive railroad system in South Carolina; the other was your own likeness. If you have no copy and want it, I will mail it to you with pleasure."

---

172   STUDY
1878, signed on plate: Butterfly (lower left). W1, 10¾ x 5⅞. 8 proofs.

173   STUDY
1878, signed on plate: Butterfly (center left). W2, 9 x 9¼. A lithotint, 12 proofs.

174   LIMEHOUSE (State I)
1878, signed on plate: Butterfly (lower right). W4, 6¾ x 10⅜. A lithotint. 35 proofs.

Drawn at Limehouse on the stone direct. Published in "Notes."

175   NOCTURNE
1878, signed on plate: Butterfly (lower right); signed in margin: Butterfly (bottom, in pencil). W5, 6¾ x 10⅛. A lithotint. 100 proofs.

The Thames at Battersea. Published in "Notes."

176   THE TOILET (State II)
1878, signed on plate: Butterfly (center left); signed: Butterfly (bottom, in pencil). W6, 10⅛ x 6½. A lithotint.

Drawn for "Piccadilly" and published in July, 1878.

176

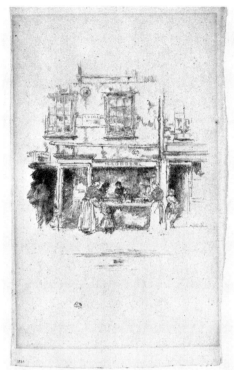

182

177   EARLY MORNING (State I)

1878, signed on plate: Butterfly (lower left).
W7, 6½ x 10¼. A lithotint. About 12 proofs.

The Thames at Battersea. Drawn for "Piccadilly" on the same stone as No. 176, and printed, but never published.

178   THE TALL BRIDGE

1878, signed on plate: Butterfly (center right).
W9, 11¼ x 7½. A lithotint. 12 proofs.

Only a few fine proofs on Japanese paper mounted. Drawn for "Piccadilly" but, although printed, not published.

179   READING (State I)

1879, signed on plate: Butterfly (lower right).
W13, 9¾ x 14½. 100 proofs.

Published in "Notes."

180   THE FAN

1879, signed on plate: Butterfly (center right).
W14, 8⅛ x 6¼. 10 proofs.

181   THE WINGED HAT (State II)

1890, signed on plate: Butterfly (center left).
W25, 7 x 6¾. 22 proofs.

Published in the "Whirlwind."

182   MAUNDER'S FISH-SHOP, CHELSEA

1890, signed on plate: Butterfly (above store sign); signed in margin: Butterfly (bottom, in pencil). W28, 7½ x 6¾. 28 proofs.

Published in the "Whirlwind."

183   THE LITTLE NUDE MODEL READING

1890, signed on plate: Butterfly (center right); signed in margin: Butterfly (bottom, in pencil). W29, 6⅝ x 7. 28 proofs.

185

184 THE HOROSCOPE

1890, signed on plate: Butterfly (center right); signed in margin: Butterfly (bottom left, in pencil). W32, 6⅜ x 6¼. 6 proofs.

185 THE GARDEN

1891, signed on plate: Butterfly (on table cloth); signed in margin: Butterfly (bottom, in pencil). W38, 6¾ x 7⅜. 6 proofs.

The names of those forming this group in the garden of Mr. Whistler's house at Cheyne Walk are Mrs. Brandon Thomas at the left of the settee, Mr. Starr and Mr. Brandon Thomas at the right end, Mr. Walter Sickert standing between them, and on the right Mrs. Whistler and Miss Philip, seated.

186 THE STEPS, LUXEMBOURG GARDENS

1893, signed on plate: Butterfly (center right); signed in margin: Butterfly (bottom, in pencil). W43, 8¼ x 6¾. 15 proofs.

187 CONVERSATION UNDER THE STATUE, LUXEMBOURG GARDENS

1893, signed on plate: Butterfly (lower right); signed in margin: Butterfly (bottom, in pencil). W44, 6¾ x 6. 15 proofs.

188 THE PANTHEON, FROM THE TERRACE OF THE LUXEMBOURG GARDENS

1893, signed on plate: Butterfly (lower left); signed in margin: Butterfly (bottom, in pencil). W45, 7⅛ x 6⅜. 15 proofs.

The Charles Deering Collection.

189 THE LONG GALLERY, LOUVRE

1894, signed on plate: Butterfly (center bottom). W52, 8½ x 6. 28 proofs.

Published in the "Studio."

188

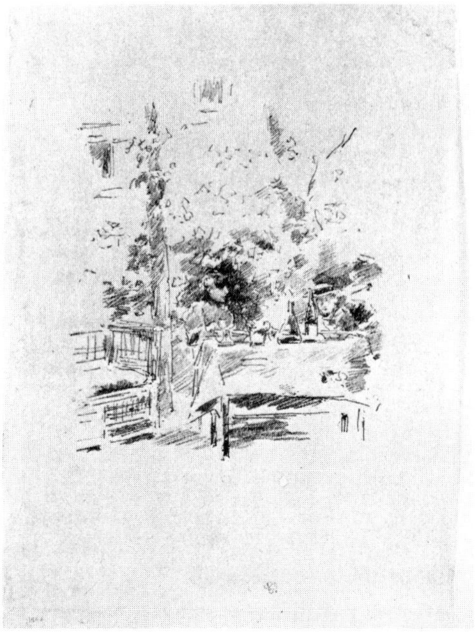

190

190 TÊTE-À-TÊTE IN THE GARDEN

1894, signed on plate: Butterfly (on table cloth); signed in margin: Butterfly (bottom, in pencil). W54, 7⅝ x 6½. 28 proofs.

191 CONFIDENCES IN THE GARDEN

1894, signed on plate: Butterfly (center right); signed in margin: Butterfly (bottom, in pencil). W60, 8⅜ x 6⅜. 28 proofs.

The Charles Deering Collection.

192 LA JOLIE NEW YORKAISE

1894, signed on plate: Butterfly (center left); signed in margin: Butterfly (bottom, in pencil). W61, 9 x 6. 25 proofs.

193 LA BELLE JARDINIÈRE

1894, signed on plate: Butterfly (center right); signed in margin: Butterfly (bottom, in pencil). W63, 8⅞ x 6¼. 25 proofs.

194 STÉPHANE MALLARMÉ

1894, signed on plate: Butterfly (lower right). W66, 3¾ x 2¾.

Drawn for a frontispiece to the poet's works and printed in Paris.

195 LA ROBE ROUGE

1894, signed on plate: Butterfly (center left); signed in margin: Butterfly (bottom right, in pencil). W68, 7⅜ x 6. 23 proofs.

Published in the "Studio."

196 LA BELLE DAME ENDORMIE

1894, signed: Butterfly (upper left). W69, 7¾ x 6⅛. 42 proofs.

197 LA FRUITIÈRE DE LA RUE DE GRENELLE

1894, signed on plate: Butterfly (center right); signed in margin: Butterfly (bottom, in pencil). W70, 9 x 6⅛. 33 proofs.

191

192

**198 THE SMITH—PASSAGE DU
       DRAGON (State I)**

1894, signed on plate: Butterfly (center left);
signed in margin: Butterfly (bottom, in pencil).
W73, 9 x 6⅜. 34 proofs.

**199 THE PRIEST'S HOUSE, ROUEN
       (State I)**

1894, signed on plate: Butterfly (center right).
W74, 9¼ x 6¼. About 12 proofs.

The Charles Deering Collection.

**200 A PORTRAIT—MISS HOWELLS
       (State II)**

1895, signed on plate: Butterfly (center right);
signed in margin: Butterfly (bottom, in pencil).
W75, 8⅞ x 6¾.

201 WALTER SICKERT

1895, signed on plate: Butterfly (center left);
signed in margin: Butterfly (bottom right, in
pencil). W79, 7¼ x 5½. 6 proofs.

202 FATHER AND SON

1895, signed on plate: Butterfly (upper left);
signed in margin: Butterfly (bottom, in pencil).
W87, 8⅛ x 6. 15 proofs.

203 YELLOW HOUSE, LANNION

1893, signed on plate: Butterfly (center right);
signed in margin: Butterfly (bottom, in pencil).
W101, 9½ x 6¼.

204 STUDY—JOSEPH PENNELL

1896, signed on plate: Butterfly (center left);
signed in margin: Butterfly (bottom, in pencil).
W111, 7¾ x 4⅛. 6 proofs.

193

200

205 LITTLE DOROTHY

1896, signed on plate: Butterfly (center left);
signed in margin: Butterfly (bottom, in pencil).
W115, 7½ x 5⅜. 4 proofs.

206 CHARING CROSS RAILWAY
BRIDGE

1896, signed on plate: Butterfly (center left);
signed in margin: Butterfly (bottom, in pencil).
W120, 5⅛ x 8⅜. 27 proofs.

The Surrey side of the bridge and the Lion
Brewery are seen from an upper story of the
Savoy Hotel. Beyond the bridge are seen St.
Thomas' Hospital and Westminster Bridge,
and, in the foreground, the Embankment.

207 THE THAMES (State I)

1896, signed on plate: Butterfly (lower right).
W125, 10½ x 7⅝.

The Clarence Buckingham Collection.

A lithotint of the river, from an upper room in
the Savoy Hotel, with the group of buildings
and Shot Tower of the Surrey side lying between Waterloo and Charing Cross bridges.

208 COUNT ROBERT DE
MONTESQUIOU. No. 2

1895. W138, 8¼ x 3¾.

209 THE GARDEN PORCH

1894, signed on plate: Butterfly (at bottom);
signed in margin: Butterfly (below, in pencil).
W140, 7⅜ x 6¼. 8 proofs.

203

210 PORTRAIT OF DR. WHISTLER.
    No. 2

1895, signed in margin: Butterfly (at bottom, in pencil). W142, 7½ x 6. 12 proofs.

211 UNFINISHED SKETCH OF LADY HADEN

1895, signed on plate: Butterfly (upper left). W143, 11⅞ x 7¾. 6 proofs.

The Charles Deering Collection.

212 AFTERNOON TEA

c. 1893, signed on plate: Butterfly (center right); signed in margin (bottom left, in pencil). W147, 7½ x 6½.

Mrs. Philip and Mrs. Charles Whibley.

212

WHISTLERIANA

AUBREY VINCENT BEARDSLEY (English, 1872-1898)

213 PORTRAIT OF WHISTLER IN SPANISH 17th CENTURY COSTUME.
Pen and india ink; 3 x 3-5/16 in.
Owned by The Art Institute of Chicago, The Walter S. Brewster Collection.

Collections: Pickford Waller, London; Walter S. Brewster, Chicago (given to Art Institute, 1933).

Bibliography: Bon-Mots of Samuel Foote and Theodore Hook, edited by Walter Jerrold and published by J. M. Dent, London, 1894, repr. p. 190; see Pennell, 1908, II, pp. 140-141; Gallatin, 1913, No. 158, repr. between pp. 48-49; Gallatin, 1918, No. 216, repr. between pp. 72-73, and p. 19; Albert E. Gallatin, *Aubrey Beardsley, Catalogue of Drawings and Bibliography,* New York, 1945, pp. 3, 36-37.

No title is given this caricature. Original drawing for one of a series of "grotesques" drawn by Beardsley for reproduction by line-block in *Bon-Mots* of Samuel Foote and Theodore Hook, published in London in March 1894. The drawings display extensive powers of invention and cover a wide range of subjects including pierrots, demons, fauns, monkeys, owls, crabs, cats, insects, and a caricature of Max Beerbohm. Though he subsequently grew to like Beardsley and his work, Whistler, when he first met him during the summer of 1893 in Paris, had little sympathy for him and he told Joseph Pennell, "Look at him!—he's just like his drawings—he's all hairs and peacock plumes—. . . ." To Joseph Pennell, incidentally, goes the credit, if not for discovering at least for giving Aubrey Beardsley his first public notice in a "glowing eulogy" published in *The Studio,* April 1893.

GIOVANNI BOLDINI (Italian, 1844-1931)

214 PORTRAIT OF JAMES McNEILL WHISTLER.
Oil on canvas; 67⅛ x 37-3/16 in. Signed lower left: Boldini/1897.
Lent by The Brooklyn Museum, Brooklyn, New York.

Collection: presented by A. Augustus Healy to the Brooklyn Museum, 1910.

Exhibitions: Paris, Exposition Universelle, 1900 (No. 10 in Italian section); Chicago 1934 (No. 415).

Bibliography: Duret, 1904, p. 180, repr. frontispiece; Camille Mauclair, *Art et Décoration,* XVIII, October 1905, pp. 151-152, repr. p. 147; Pennell, 1908, II, p. 193; W. H. Goodyear, *The Museum News,* The Brooklyn Institute of Arts and Sciences, V, No. 6, March 1910, pp. 77-80; Gallatin, 1913, pp. 28-29, No. 51; Gallatin, 1918, pp. 17-18, 39, No. 58, repr. between pp. 40-41; Pennell, 1921, repr. f. p. 18.

Whistler disliked to pose; he also disliked Boldini's portrait of him, and said he hoped he did not look like that. In the words of Pennell, the portrait "is, however, a wonderful presentment of him in his very worst mood, and . . . he was in his worst mood all the while he posed. It is the Whistler whom the world knew and feared." Edward G. Kennedy, the art dealer and intimate friend of Whistler, was present in Boldini's studio at the time of Whistlers' final sitting for the portrait, and he subsequently told Albert Gallatin (quoted in Gallatin, 1918, p. 18) that

Whistler's dislike of the portrait, and consequently of Boldini, may have been due to the fact that the portrait was so "extraordinarily" and so "startlingly" resemblant. "He always wanted to be depicted as over six feet high and to look like a Major-General." Boldini's picture won the medal of honor in the Italian section of the Universal Exposition of 1900.

215 WHISTLER ASLEEP.
Dry-point; 7⅞ x 12 in. Date: 1897.
Owned by The Art Institute of Chicago, The Walter S. Brewster Collection.

Collections: Walter S. Brewster, Chicago, 1914 (purchased from Edward G. Kennedy, New York); given by Walter S. Brewster to Art Institute, 1933.

Exhibitions: Chicago 1917 (No. 287); Chicago 1923 (No. 39).

Bibliography: Pennell, 1908, II, p. 193; Gallatin, 1913, see No. 55; Gallatin, 1918, pp. 17-18, 50, No. 127, repr. between pp. 58-59.

Gallatin (1918, pp. 17-18) informs us that Boldini sketched the dry-point on the copper after Whistler's last sitting for the full-length portrait now in the Brooklyn Museum (see No. 214 in this exhibition) and that it was done immediately after lunch, in about fifteen minutes, while Whistler was indulging in his habitual nap.

WALTER GREAVES (English, 1841-1930)

216 JAMES McNEILL WHISTLER.
Oil on canvas; 32⅞ x 22⅞ in. Signed lower right: W. Greaves/1869.
Owned by The Art Institute of Chicago, A. A. Munger Collection.

Collection: Scott & Fowles, Ltd., New York; purchased for the Art Institute, 1926.

Exhibitions: Chicago 1933 (No. 265); Chicago 1934 (No. 416).

Bibliography: see Pennell, 1921, pp. 140-142, and repr. f. p. 142; *Bulletin of the Art Institute of Chicago*, XX, No. 5, May 1926, p. 65, repr.

Walter Greaves and his brother Henry were boatsmen who rowed Whistler about the Thames while he made sketches, carried his painting materials and worked in his studio. They became his pupils, and of the two, Walter attained some degree of recognition. His work is a rather clumsy but beguiling composite of his own *naïf* style and Whistler's sophisticated example. Greaves painted innumerable portraits of Whistler, which look very much alike, and Pennell (*loc. cit.*, entry in *Journal* for 4 May, 1911) suggests that they were all done in the 1880's, though some are dated between 1869 and 1876, because of the hat with the straight brim (shown in some of the portraits) which Whistler began to wear in 1885 after he saw William M. Chase wearing one. "Had Whistler sat for them, [the portraits] it would have taken years of his life and almost all are in the supposed costume of the same period, even to the hat. . . . There is no evidence of Whistler ever having posed to Greaves at all. Whistler never referred to having posed, none of these pictures was ever shown or even heard of during his lifetime so far as we know. . . . Some of Greaves' portraits bear a striking resemblance to contemporary photographs and the caricatures by Spy and Ape." Gallatin (1918, p. 14) questions the *status* of these portraits, adding that after Whistler's death, Greaves "fell into the hands of one or two obscure dealers who commissioned him to turn out paintings and drawings of Whistler in an unceasing stream," and that many of these were executed expressly for the "jolly Americans."

PAUL CÉSAR FRANÇOIS HELLEU (French, 1850-1927)

217 PORTRAIT OF WHISTLER.

Dry-point printed in black ink on laid blue paper (possibly taken from end paper of old book); 13¼ x 10 in. Inscribed upper left: 12 mai 97, and on reverse in brown ink in 18th century hand: Regl de Salis/Grisoy [?]/19.
Owned by The Art Institute of Chicago, The Charles Deering Collection.

Bibliography: La Revue de l'Art ancien et moderne, XIV, No. 81, December 1903, repr. f. p. 444; Pennell, 1908, II, p. 193; Gallatin, 1913, No. 54; Robert de Montesquiou, *Paul Helleu Peintre et Graveur,* Paris, 1913, p. 48; Gallatin, 1918, pp. 17, 50, No. 125, repr. between pp. 58-59; Pennell, 1921, repr. between pp. 18-19.

Helleu, a fashionable and prolific portraitist during the *fin de siècle* era in Paris, executed portraits of over fifteen-hundred women and children, but only about four of men, these being Edmond de Goncourt, Whistler, Montesquiou and Rouart. This dry-point portrait of Whistler was done at the time Boldini was painting Whistler's portrait (see No. 214 in this exhibition) and in pose is almost identical with it. In his book on Helleu, Montesquiou remarks that the dry-point shows Whistler "tel un chat tigre spirituel, un oeil clair sous son monocle, l'autre pétillant de malice." Whistler, however, disliked it as much as he did the painted and dry-point portraits of himself by Boldini.

WYNCIE KING (American, 1884-   )

218 JOSEPH PENNELL WITH WHISTLER.

Watercolor over pencil; 13¼ x 9¼ in. Signed bottom left in pencil heightened with red coloring: Wyncie King, and inscribed below in pencil: Joseph Pennell.
Date: not later than 1923.
Owned by The Art Institute of Chicago, The Walter S. Brewster Collection.

Collections: F. S. Bigelow (owner in 1925); Walter S. Brewster, Chicago (given to Art Institute, 1933).

Exhibition: The Third International Watercolor Exhibition, The Art Institute of Chicago, 20 March - 22 April, 1923, No. 188.

Bibliography: The Third International Watercolor Exhibition (exhibition catalogue), The Art Institute of Chicago, 1923, No. 188, repr. p. 21; *The American Art News,* XXI, No. 32, May 19, 1923, p. 6, repr.; Joseph Pennell, *The Adventures of an Illustrator,* Boston, 1925, repr. p. 311.

An enormously tall and unprepossessing Joseph Pennell pulls a small cart on which stands a diminutive and insectiform Whistler with butterfly wings. Joseph Pennell (1860-1926) and his wife Elizabeth (1855-1936) are that diligent and tenacious American couple who got to know Whistler well in the middle of the 1890's and who, having made themselves his Boswell, wrote the monumental *Life* which was published five years after the artist's death.

MORTIMER MENPES (English, 1860-1929)

219 WHISTLER.
Dry-point; 7-3/16 x 5-3/8 in. Signed bottom right: Mortimer Menpes imp. Date: 1884-1886.
Owned by The Art Institute of Chicago, The Walter S. Brewster Collection.

Collections: Howard Mansfield, New York; Walter S. Brewster, Chicago, 1916 (bought from Walter M. Hill, Chicago); given by Walter S. Brewster to Art Institute, 1933.

Exhibitions: Chicago 1917 (No. 290); Chicago 1923 (No. 28).

Bibliography: see Pennell, 1908, II, pp. 18-20; Dorothy Menpes, "Mortimer Menpes, Colorist," *The Booklovers Magazine*, III, No. 1, January 1904, p. 59, Elmer Adler, *Catalogue of an Exhibition of Portraitures of James McNeill Whistler from the Whistleriana of Elmer Adler,* The Memorial Art Gallery, Rochester, New York, 1915, p. 49; Gallatin, 1918, No. 163; see Joseph Pennell, *The Adventures of an Illustrator,* Boston, 1925, p. 241.

Mortimer Menpes, born in Australia, painter, engraver, essayist, wrote a book on Whistler entitled *Whistler as I knew him* (published in London, 1904) in which he stated that among Whistler's many "Followers" were only two genuine pupils: Walter Sickert and himself. Menpes met Whistler in late 1880 after the latter's return from Venice and thereupon forgot about Edward J. Poynter with whom he was sudying at the South Kensington Schools to become "almost a slave" in Whistler's service. Whistler eventually quarrelled with his ardent disciple Menpes and broke off their friendship sometime during the late 1880's. Menpes, however, retained his liking for Whistler and his daughter Dorothy (*loc. cit.*) related rather pathetically that "Menpes sat at Whistler's feet with an artistic reverence that has never grown less, though their harmonies at a later period ceased to blend." Other writers showed less sympathy. According to Elmer Adler (*loc. cit.*) Whistler developed a "great horror" of Menpes's writing his life, and Joseph Pennell (*loc. cit.*) characterized Menpes as a "slave and a slavey . . ."

SIR WILLIAM NICHOLSON (English, 1872-1949)

220 PORTRAIT OF WHISTLER STANDING.
Lithograph reproduction of a woodcut; 9-11/16 x 8-7/8 in. Inscribed at bottom: James McNeill Whistler. Date: 1897.
Owned by The Art Institute of Chicago, The Walter S. Brewster Collection.

Collections: Walter S. Brewster, Chicago, 1915 (bought from Walter M. Hill, Chicago); given by Walter S. Brewster to Art Institute, 1933.

Exhibitions: Chicago 1917 (No. 295); Chicago 1923 (No. 41).

Bibliography: Pennell, 1908, II, p. 194; Gallatin, 1913, see No. 116; Gallatin, 1918, p. 18, and No. 139; Lillian Browse, *William Nicholson*, London, 1956, pp. 16-17.

Reprinted from a woodcut done as part of a series beginning with the Jubilee woodcut of Queen Victoria with her dog, for the *New Review* (Vol. XVII) of which W. E. Henley was editor. Afterwards included in the artist's *Twelve Portraits,* London, 1899, published by William Heinemann. The inscription "James McNeill

Whistler" did not appear on the original woodcut. William Heinemann was Whistler's publisher and one of the most faithful of his friends during the latter part of his life. It was at Heinemann's instance that Whistler and William Nicholson first met in 1897 at his cottage in Hampton where they were fellow guests for a week-end and that Nicholson undertook the woodcut portrait of Whistler. William Nicholson, who attained renown as a painter of portraits and still-lifes of Post-Impressionist tendency, was the father of Ben Nicholson, the leading representative of abstract constructivist painting in Britain today; he was also at one time the father-in-law of the poet Robert Graves.

CARLO PELLEGRINI (Ape) (Italian, 1838-1889)

221 WHISTLER No. 3.
Dry-point, printed in black ink; 11-7/8 x 7-13/16 in. Signed lower right in pencil: Carlo Pellegrini no 3, and upper left in pencil: Ape.
Owned by The Art Institute of Chicago, The Walter S. Brewster Collection.

Collection: Walter S. Brewster, Chicago, acquired 1931 (given to Art Institute, 1933).

Bibliography: see Duret, 1904, pp. 140-142, Pennell, 1908, II, p. 12, Pennell, 1920, p. 158.

Carlo Pellegrini was a Neapolitan transplanted in London where he achieved considerable success in the field of caricatural portraiture. His work, published in the form of lithographs which he signed "Ape," in *Vanity Fair*, was held in high esteem by Whistler with whom he was on very friendly terms. Pellegrini did several caricatures of Whistler, including a large painting, a full-length Whistler in evening dress, which once belonged to John W. Simpson, New York.

WALTER RICHARD SICKERT (English, 1860-1942)

222 PORTRAIT OF WHISTLER.
Pen and india ink; 12⅜ x 10⅛ in. Signed bottom right in brown ink: Sickert. Chelsea 1900.
Owned by The Art Institute of Chicago, The Walter S. Brewster Collection.

Collections: Count Robert de Montesquiou-Fezensac; Walter S. Brewster, Chicago, 1922 (bought from Albert Roullier, Chicago); given by Walter S. Brewster to Art Institute, 1933.

Exhibition: Chicago 1923 (No. 44).

Bibliography: see Andrew Dempsey, "Whistler and Sickert: a friendship and its end," *Apollo*, LXXXIII, No. 47, January 1966, pp. 30-37.

Sickert met Whistler in 1882 and at the invitation of the latter he left the Slade School where he was studying with Alphonse Legros to become Whistler's pupil and assistant. Their friendship lasted until 1896 and was brought to an end by Sickert's involvement in the quarrel between Whistler and Sir William Eden (the affair of "The Baronet and the Butterfly") and the subsequent Pennell-Sickert lithography case, which Pennell won on evidence provided by Whistler. In spite of the break in their association, Whistler seems to have continued to take an interest in the activities of his former pupil, and it is to Sickert, who apparently retained no bitter feelings, that we owe some of the most perceptive comments on Whistler. These occurred chiefly in the form of articles written for newspapers and magazines, many of which, edited by Osbert Sitwell, have been included in a volume of Sickert's writings called *A Free House!*, published in London, 1947.

LESLIE WARD (Spy) (English, 1851-1922)

223 "A SYMPHONY" (PORTRAIT OF WHISTLER).
Lithograph in color; 12-1/16 x 7-1/4 in. Date: 1878.
Owned by The Art Institute of Chicago, The Walter S. Brewster Collection.

Collections: Walter S. Brewster, Chicago, 1914 (bought from Edward G. Kennedy, New York); given by Walter S. Brewster to Art Institute, 1933.

Exhibitions: Chicago 1917 (No. 279); Chicago 1923 (No. 21).

Bibliography: Duret, 1904, p. 142, repr. p. 143; Pennell, 1908, I, p. 217; Gallatin, 1913, No. 145; Leslie Ward, *Forty Years of 'Spy'*, London, 1915, pp. 298-299; Gallatin, 1918, No. 242, repr. between pp. 72-73; Pennell, 1921, p. 184.

Leslie Ward, who drew caricatures for *Vanity Fair* under the pseudonym of "Spy," was commissioned by that newspaper to do a caricature of Whistler and it was reproduced on 12 January, 1878. A preliminary drawing for the lithograph is in the National Portrait Gallery, London. In his book of reminiscences Ward *(loc. cit.)* included the following description of Whistler: "Somewhere about the same period I did Whistler, who was an excellent subject, but his unlimited peculiarities lay more in his gesture and speech and habits. I never went to a social function at which he was present without hearing his caustic, nasal little laugh, . . . raised at the wrong moment. . . . At the same time there was something quite irresistible about the fascination of the man. He lived in a house in Tite Street on the Chelsea Embankment . . . . and every one who had the opportunity breakfasted with him when invited, although the menu usually consisted of a sardine and a cup of coffee."

THOMAS R. WAY (English, 1861-1913)

224 PORTRAIT OF WHISTLER.
Lithograph; 8 x 5½ in. Signed lower left: T. R. W., and bottom right in pencil: T. R. Way. Date: 1895.
Owned by The Art Institute of Chicago, The Walter S. Brewster Collection.

Collections: Walter S. Brewster, Chicago, 1915 (bought from Albert Roullier, Chicago); given by Walter S. Brewster to Art Institute, 1933.

Exhibitions: Chicago 1917 (No. 285); Chicago 1923 (No. 36).

Bibliography: Gallatin, 1913, No. 112; Gallatin, 1918, No. 131; see Pennell, 1921, pp. 105-106.

Thomas R. Way, lithographer, author of several books on Whistler including a catalogue of Whistler's lithographs which was first published in 1896, with a second edition appearing in 1905. Way printed many of Whistler's pamphlets and lithographs for him, and he was unrivalled in his knowledge of the lithographs. Whistler had met T. R. Way and his father Thomas Way through work connected with the Peacock Room (1877) and it was Thomas Way who, in 1878, introduced Whistler to the methods in use in lithography with the result that Whistler made his first experiments in lithography during that year.

SAMUEL JOHNSON WOOLF (American, 1880-1948).

225   PORTRAIT OF WHISTLER.
Lithograph; 9¾ x 12⅞ in. Signed lower right in pencil: S. J. Woolf.
Owned by The Art Institute of Chicago, The Walter S. Brewster Collection.

Collections: Walter S. Brewster, Chicago, purchased 1928; given by Walter S. Brewster to Art Institute, 1933.

Samuel Johnson Woolf, an artist-journalist, was widely known for a type of reportage called the combination portrait sketch and interview, which was published in the New York *Times* and many other periodicals. He acquired an early reputation as a portrait painter and a lithographer—he made lithographic portraits of such personages as Mark Twain and Theodore Roosevelt—but his career, after the first World War, was devoted to interviewing and drawing celebrities in Europe and the United States.

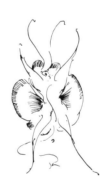